Scott Foresman - Addison Wesley
MIDDLE SCHOOL MATH

Problem-Solving Masters

For Guided Problem Solving

Course 3

Scott Foresman - Addison Wesley

Editorial Offices: Menlo Park, California • Glenview, Illinois
Sales Offices: Reading, Massachusetts • Atlanta, Georgia • Glenview, Illinois
Carrollton, Texas • Menlo Park, California

http://www.sf.aw.com

ISBN 0-201-31275-1

Printed in the United States of America

1 2 3 4 5 6 7 8 9 10 – BW – 02 01 00 99 98 97

Contents

Chapter 11: Similarity, Congruence, and Transformations

Chapter 12: Counting and Probability

Overview

Problem-Solving Masters (For Guided Problem Solving) provide a step-by-step approach to solve a problem selected from the student book. These selections are made from the *Practice and Apply* section or from the *Problem Solving and Reasoning* section. Some of these selections are routine in nature and cover basic concepts. Others are nonroutine and might involve multiple-step problems, problems with too much information, problems involving critical thinking, and so on. An icon in the Teacher's Edition flags the selected problem so that the teacher will know what problem is provided on the master.

How to use

The Problem-Solving Masters are designed so that the teacher can use them in many different ways:

a. As a teaching tool to guide students in exploring and mastering a specific problem-solving skill or strategy. Making a transparency of the worksheet provides an excellent way to expedite this process as students work along with the teacher at their desks.

b. As additional practice in solving problems for students who have had difficulty in completing the assignment.

c. As independent or group work to help students reach a better understanding of the problem-solving process.

d. As a homework assignment that may encourage students to involve their parents in the educational process.

Description of the master

The problem to be solved is stated at the top of each master. The master is then divided into the four steps of the Problem-Solving Guidelines that are used throughout the student text. Each step includes key questions designed to guide students through the problem-solving process. At the bottom of the master, *Solve Another Problem* allows students to use their skills to solve a problem similar to the original problem. This helps reinforce the problem-solving skills and strategies they have just used in solving the problem on the master.

The Guided Problem Solving master on the next page can be used to help students organize their work as they complete the *Solve Another Problem.* It may also be used to assist students in solving any problem as they complete the four steps of the Problem-Solving Guidelines.

1. **Understand** ensures that students are able to interpret the problem and determine key facts.

2. **Plan** actively involves students in devising a plan or strategy for solving the problem. They may be asked to choose a fact or formula that could be used to solve the problem. In other cases, students may be asked to model the problem or draw a picture. Other times, students will be asked to choose a strategy they can use to solve the problem. Problem-solving strategies often used include: Look for a Pattern, Make a Table, Work Backward, Draw a Diagram, Make an Organized List, Guess and Check, Use Logical Reasoning, and Solve a Simpler Problem.

3. **Solve** encourages students to carry out the plan and arrive at an answer. Students may be asked to answer the question using a full sentence.

4. **Look Back** encourages students to review their work and check their answer to see if it is reasonable. This step often asks students to reflect on the strategy they used or to suggest other strategies they could also have used to solve the problem. It is important that students think of this step as a natural part of the problem-solving process.

Name ____________________

Guided Problem Solving

Understand

Plan

Solve

Look Back

Name ______________________________

Guided Problem Solving
1-1

GPS PROBLEM 8, STUDENT PAGE 10

When the city schools take a two-week winter holiday, a skating rink gives students under 18 a discount to skate on weekdays. Make a stem-and-leaf diagram using a table which shows the daily number of students that take advantage of this discount. What days are represented in the stem with the most leaves?

Mon.	Tue.	Wed.	Thur.	Fri.	Mon.	Tue.	Wed.	Thur.	Fri.
64	52	57	51	42	44	39	42	52	55

Understand

1. Circle the way you are asked to display the data.
2. Underline what you are asked to find.

Plan

3. List the data in order from least to greatest.

____

4. What is the range of data? ______________

Solve

Stem	Leaf

5. Arrange the stems in numerical order.
6. List the ones digits of each stem in increasing order.
7. Which stem has the most leaves? ________
8. Name the days represented in the stem with the most leaves.

____

Look Back

9. How can you be sure you have recorded all the data? ______________

____

SOLVE ANOTHER PROBLEM

Make a stem-and-leaf diagram of the quiz scores below. Which quizzes are represented in the stem with the most leaves? ______________

Quiz	1	2	3	4	5	6	7	8	9	10
Score	95	75	63	77	89	99	75	84	81	81

Stem	Leaf

Name ______________________________

Guided Problem Solving 1-2

GPS PROBLEM 5, STUDENT PAGE 15

Find the mean, median, and mode for the data set.

During 1982–1990, the annual number of oil tanker spills worldwide was 9, 17, 15, 9, 8, 12, 13, 31, and 8. Identify the outlier and calculate the mean and median as if the outlier were not in the data set.

Understand

1. Circle the data set.

2. What is an outlier? ______________________

Plan

3. List the data in order from least to greatest.

____

4. How many data values are in the data set? ____________

Solve

5. For the data set of oil tanker spills from 1982–1990, find the

a. mean. __________ b. median. __________ c. mode. __________

6. What is the outlier? __________

7. What is the mean without the outlier as part of the data? __________

8. What is the median without the outlier as part of the data? __________

Look Back

9. How did the mean and median change when you calculated them without the outlier? Why? ______________________

____

SOLVE ANOTHER PROBLEM

Find the mean, median, and mode of the data set naming the number of minutes some students spent on chores last night: 18, 24, 47, 31, 21, 29. Identify the outlier and calculate the mean and median as if the outlier were not in the data set. __________________

____

____

Name ______________________________

Guided Problem Solving
1-3

 **PROBLEM 2, STUDENT PAGE 20**

Sketch a box-and-whisker plot for the set of data. Between what values does the middle half of the data fall?

During the 1980s, the largest major earthquakes around the world registered 7.3, 7.2, 7.7, 7.1, 7.8, 8.1, 7.3, 6.5, 7.3, 6.8, and 6.9 on the Richter Scale.

Understand

1. Circle the information you need to sketch a box-and-whiskers plot.

Plan

2. Arrange the data in order from least to greatest.

____

3. What is the range? ______________ The median? ________

4. What is the median of the lower half? ________ Of the upper half? ________

Solve

5. Draw the box-and-whisker plot using the range, the median, and the lower and the upper quartiles for the data. Write a title.

6. Between what values does the middle half fall? ______________

Look Back

7. What other ways could you display the data? ______________

SOLVE ANOTHER PROBLEM

Sketch a box-and-whisker plot for the set of data showing the days spent on lab projects: 34, 32, 50, 16, 29, 37, 44, 29, 18, 22, 40 and 32. Between what values does the middle half of the data fall? ______________

Name ______________________________

Guided Problem Solving
1-4

PROBLEM 4, STUDENT PAGE 26

Draw a line graph of the average monthly production of cars (in thousands) from 1986 to 1992. About how many cars were made in 1990?

Year	1986	1987	1988	1989	1990	1991	1992
Cars	474	451	504	567	592	590	626

Understand

1. What kind of graph do you need to draw? ______________

Plan

2. Which operation will you use to find yearly production? ______________
3. How will you scale the vertical axis? Why might you have a break in the scale? ______________
4. How will you scale the horizontal axis? ______________

Solve

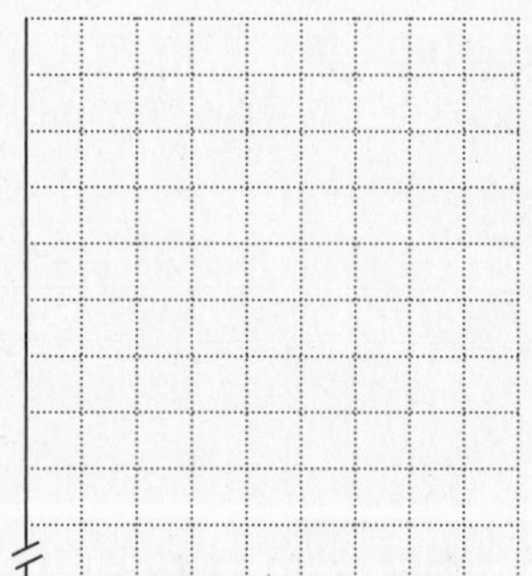

5. Scale the axes.
6. Plot the number of cars produced each year and draw a line through each point, connecting them.
7. Label each axis and title the graph.
8. About how many cars were made in 1990? ______________

Look Back

9. Would the graph be easier to read with or without a break in the scale? Explain. ______________

SOLVE ANOTHER PROBLEM

There were 5,961,000 cars produced in 1993. Find the average monthly production and add this data to your line graph above. ______________

Name ______________________________

Guided Problem Solving 1-5

GPS PROBLEM 5, STUDENT PAGE 35

State the population and whether or not the sample is random.

For the population of country music fans: randomly chosen attendees of a country music concert are asked about their favorite performers.

Understand

1. What two things are you asked to find? ______________________________

2. Who makes up the sample? ______________________________

Plan

3. How were the attendees chosen? ______________________________

4. Are the people attending the concert biased? Explain. ______________________________

Solve

5. What is the population? ______________________________

6. Is the sample representative of all country music fans? Explain. ______________________________

Look Back

7. Is the sample size representative of the population? ______________________________

SOLVE ANOTHER PROBLEM

State the population and whether or not the sample is random.

The Pep Club sold 800 raffle tickets. One stub from each ticket was placed in a bin. The bin was shaken and 5 tickets were drawn for prizes.

____

Name ____________________

Guided Problem Solving
1-6

GPS PROBLEM 2, STUDENT PAGE 40

Asteroids are chunks of rock orbiting the sun. Most of them are between the orbits of Mars and Jupiter. Astronomers have studied 105 of them to see how fast they rotate. The data is rounded to the nearest rotation and summarized in this histogram.

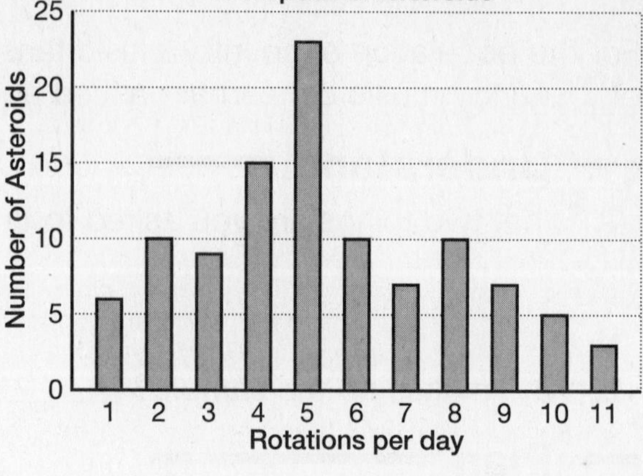

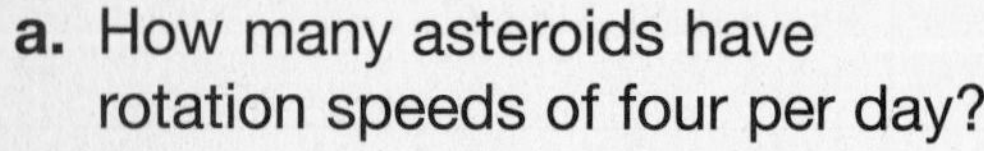

a. How many asteroids have rotation speeds of four per day?

b. Make a frequency table for this histogram.

c. What is the mode?

Understand

1. Circle what you are asked to make.

Plan

2. Label the columns in the frequency table.

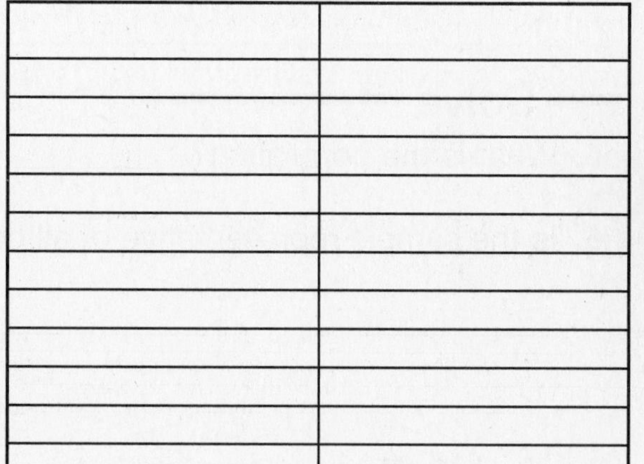

Solve

3. How many asteroids have rotation speeds of four?

____

4. Complete the frequency table.

5. What is the mode? ____________________

Look Back

6. How do you know that all data is recorded?

____

SOLVE ANOTHER PROBLEM

Absences in each of Mrs. Reynolds classes are summarized in this graph.

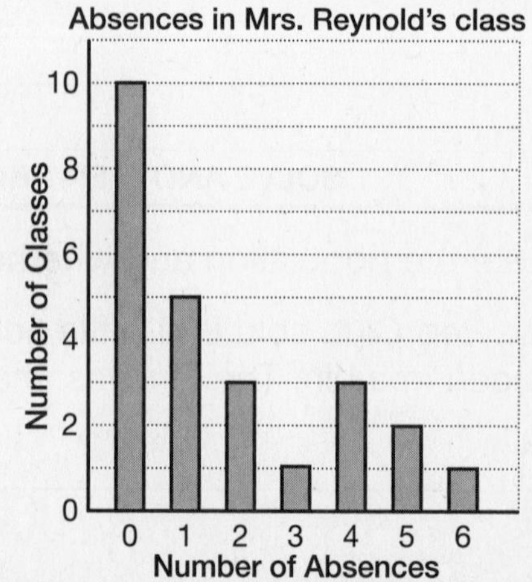

a. How many have 5 absences? ____________________

b. Make a frequency table of this data on another sheet of paper.

c. What is the mode? ____________________

Name ______________________________

Guided Problem Solving 1-7

PROBLEM 2, STUDENT PAGE 45

As people age, their sleeping habits change. Below is a table that displays daily sleep time (in hours) and age (in years). Create a scatterplot and draw a trend line for the data.

Age	1	4	6	12	10	22	18	67	82	43	51
Sleep Time	13	11	11	10.5	9	8	9	5.5	5	7.5	6

Understand

1. Underline what you asked to do.

2. How do you determine if there is a trend? ______________________________

____

Plan

3. What will the labels be for each scale?

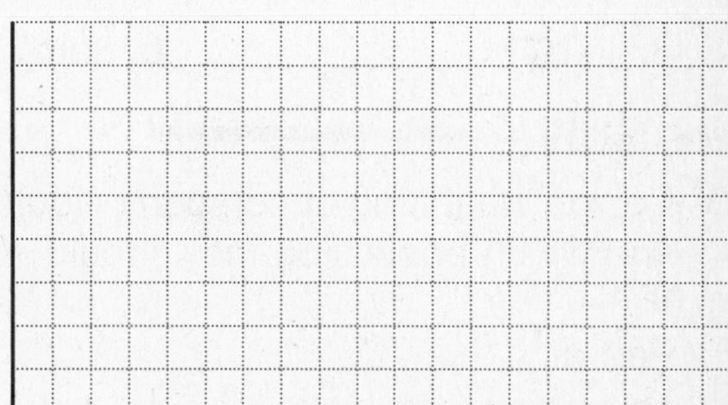

a. Horizontal ______________

b. Vertical ______________

Solve

4. Label the axes and plot the points.

5. Fit a trend line for the data.

Look Back

6. Write a sentence to describe any relationship between age and sleep time. ______________________________

____

SOLVE ANOTHER PROBLEM

Below is a table that displays average weekly allowances (in dollars) and age (in years) for some neighborhood children and teens. Create a scatterplot and draw a trend line for the data

Age	4	5	8	10	6	9	7	11	13	12
Allowance	1	1	3	4	2	4	2	5	8	9

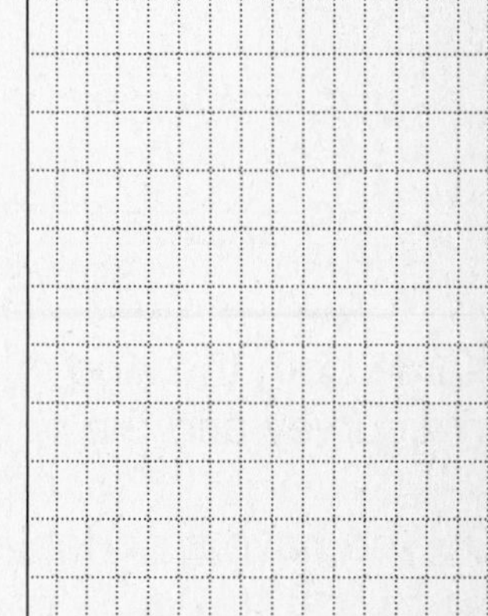

Name ______________________________

Guided Problem Solving 1-8

GPS PROBLEM 10, STUDENT PAGE 50

For each of the following questions, name both the kind of company that would use the question in a survey and the population of the survey. Explain your reasoning for each.

a. Approximately how many times per year do you get a sunburn?

b. How many headaches do you get per year?

c. How many computer video games do you play each week?

d. How long has it been since you've had a burger?

Understand

1. Underline the three things you are asked to do for each question.

Plan

2. Sunburn is the topic in part a. What is the topic in the other parts?

a. In **b**? ____________ **b.** In **c**? ____________ **c.** In **d**? ____________

Solve

3. Decide what kind of company would be asking such a question and which population they should survey. Explain your reasoning.

Part **a** ______________________________

Part **b** ______________________________

Part **c** ______________________________

Part **d** ______________________________

Look Back

4. Would a written or oral questionnaire be a better way to take the survey? Explain why it would better reach your target population. ____________

____

____

SOLVE ANOTHER PROBLEM

Name both the kind of company that would use the following question in a survey and the population of the survey. Explain your reasoning.

Do you have a portable CD or tape player? ______________________________

____

Name ______________________________

Guided Problem Solving
2-1

GPS PROBLEM 12, STUDENT PAGE 65

What integer is described by the following? The absolute value is 5 and the number is to the left of 0 on a number line.

Understand

1. Circle the information you need.
2. Underline what you are asked to find.
3. What is an integer?

   ____

4. What is absolute value?

   ____

5. Which numbers are to the left of 0? ____________

Plan

6. What points have an absolute value of 5? ________
7. Draw a number line. Label 0 and the points with absolute values of 5.

Solve

8. Two points have an absolute value of 5.
   Which point is to the left of 0 on the number line? ________
9. Answer the question using a complete sentence.

   ____

   ____

Look Back

10. Could you have found the integer without drawing a number line? How?

    ____

    ____

SOLVE ANOTHER PROBLEM

Find the integer that has an absolute value of 3 and is to the right of 0 on the number line. ________

Name ______________________________

Guided Problem Solving
2-2

GPS PROBLEM 25, STUDENT PAGE 71

An elevator on the 10th floor goes down 9 floors. Then it goes up 19 floors, down 3, and finally up 12. What floor does it end up on? Explain how you arrived at your answer.

Understand

1. Circle the information you need.
2. Underline what you are asked to find.

Plan

3. Think of the movement of the elevator as addition. Going down is shown as negative integers. Which would show the elevator going up?

   ____

4. Which will help you find the answer? ________

   a. 10 + 9 + 19 + 3 + 12   **b.** 10 + (–9) + (–19) + (–3) + (–12)

   c. 10 + (–9) + 19 + (–3) + 12

Solve

5. Add to find the floor the elevator ends up on. Use the commutative and associative properties to group integers that have the same sign.

   ____

6. Write a sentence answering the question in the problem. Then explain how you found your answer.

   ____

   ____

Look Back

7. How could you have found the answer using a different method?

   ____

SOLVE ANOTHER PROBLEM

At dawn, the temperature was 6°C above freezing. The temperature had risen 10 degrees by noon, and another 5 degrees by 3:00 P.M. before falling 12 degrees. The next morning the temperature had fallen another 6 degrees. What was the temperature the next morning?

____

Name ____________________

Guided Problem Solving
2-3

PROBLEM 17, STUDENT PAGE 75

Last week, Maria saw a dress priced at $53. The sign in the window said there was $5 off any purchase in the store. She decided to wait for a sale. This week, the dress was priced at $49 but there was no discount. She bought the dress. Should she have waited? Explain.

Understand

1. Circle the information you need.

2. Write *$5 off* as an integer. ________

Plan

3. Which expression will help you find the how much Maria would have paid for the dress with the $5 discount? ________

a. 53 + (–5) **b.** 49 + 5 **c.** 53 + 5 **d.** 49 + (–5)

Solve

4. How much would Maria have paid for the dress last week if she took $5 off the dress price of $53? ________

5. Is the amount Maria paid this week more or less than the amount she would have paid last week? ________

6. Should Maria have waited to buy the dress? Explain.

____

____

____

Look Back

7. What other number sentences could you have used to find the answer?

____

SOLVE ANOTHER PROBLEM

Cheryl saw a jacket during a pre-season sale for $15 off the regular price of $47. Today she saw the jacket priced at $35 and she bought it. Should she have bought the jacket during the pre-season sale? Explain.

____

____

____

Name ____

Guided Problem Solving
2-4

GPS PROBLEM 37, STUDENT PAGE 81

The temperature has been falling an average of 4° per hour. If the temperature at 12:00 A.M. is 10°F, what do you predict it will be at 6:00 A.M.?

Understand

1. Circle the information you need.
2. Underline the question.

Plan

3. Find the number of hours from 12:00 A.M. until 6:00 A.M. ____________
4. Write an integer for a *falling* temperature of 4°F. ________
5. Will the temperature at 6:00 A.M. be higher or lower than the 12:00 A.M. temperature? ____________
6. Which of the following is a reasonable answer? ________

   a. about 0°F **b.** below 0°F **c.** above 10°F

Solve

7. Predict how much the temperature will change between 12:00 A.M. and 6:00 A.M. ____________________
8. Predict the temperature at 6:00 A.M. ________
9. Write a sentence predicting the temperature.

____

____

Look Back

10. How could you have found the answer using a different method?

____

____

SOLVE ANOTHER PROBLEM

A water tank has been draining an average of 2 feet per hour. If the level at 8:00 A.M. is 18 feet, at what level do you think the water will be at 4:00 P.M.?

____

Name ______________________________

Guided Problem Solving
2-5

GPS PROBLEM 26, STUDENT PAGE 86

Carrie wants to bring snack food to the drama club meeting. She decides to buy 15 bagels at $0.50 each and 1 container of cream cheese for $1.50. How much will she spend?

Understand

1. Circle the information you need.
2. Underline the question.

Plan

3. Which operation will you use to find the cost of 15 bagels? ________

   a. division **b.** subtraction **c.** multiplication

4. Which of the following would be a reasonable total cost for the bagels and the cream cheese? ________

   a. about $5 **b.** about $10 **c.** about $30

Solve

5. How much did Carrie spend for 15 bagels? __________
6. How much did Carrie spend for 15 bagels and 1 container of cream cheese? __________

Look Back

7. How do you know that your answer is reasonable?

____

____

____

8. Write a number sentence that shows how you found your answer.

____

____

SOLVE ANOTHER PROBLEM

Mr. Taylor bought 24 book marks at $0.75 each for the students in his literature class. He also bought one journal for himself at $2.50. How much did he spend?

____

Name ________________________________

Guided Problem Solving
2-6

GPS PROBLEM 21, STUDENT PAGE 94

Graph a triangle with vertices (4, 6), (1, 2), and (4, 0). Graph another triangle with vertices (–4, –6), (–1, –2), and (–4, 0). How are the triangles related? How are the coordinates of their vertices related?

Understand

1. What are you asked to find?

____

____

2. How many triangles do you need to graph? ____________

Plan

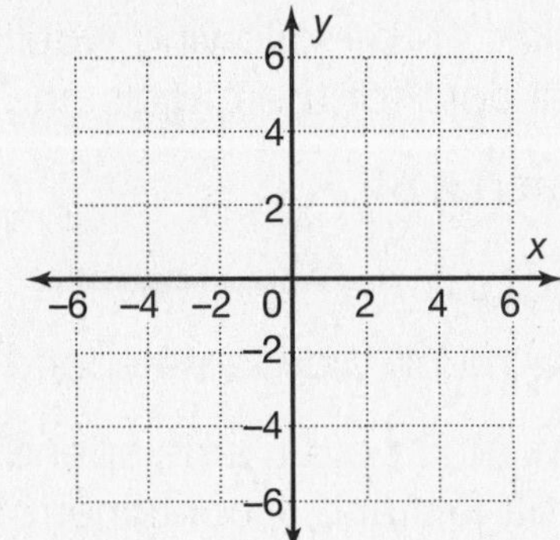

3. Plot the vertices of the first triangle and connect the points.

4. Plot the vertices of the second triangle and connect the points.

Solve

5. How do the size and shape of the triangles you graphed compare?

____

6. How are the values of the *x*-coordinates of the vertices (4, 6) and (–4, –6) related? Is this true for the other vertices?

____

Look Back

7. Does it seem reasonable that if the first triangle is in Quadrant I, then the second triangle will be in Quadrant III? Explain.

____

____

SOLVE ANOTHER PROBLEM

Graph a triangle with vertices (–3, 2), (–3, 6), and (–1, 1) on the grid above. Graph another triangle with vertices (3, –2), (3, –6), and (1, –1). How are the triangles related? How are the coordinates of their vertices related?

____

Name ______________________________

Guided Problem Solving
2-7

GPS PROBLEM 27, STUDENT PAGE 100

A square deck has an area of 121 square feet. What is the length of one side?

Understand

1. What area does the deck have? ______________

2. What shape is the deck? ______________

3. The sides of a square all have the ______________ length.

Plan

4. How can you find the area of a square if the side of the square is *n*?

____

5. Which of the following is a reasonable answer? ______

a. between 5 and 10 ft **b.** between 10 and 15 ft

6. What strategy can you use to solve the problem? ______________

Solve

7. What is the length of one side of the deck? ________

8. Write the answer in a complete sentence.

____

____

Look Back

9. How could you use your estimate to help you find the answer?

____

____

____

SOLVE ANOTHER PROBLEM

Fran put 2-ft high fencing around her square vegetable garden to keep out rabbits. The garden has an area of 225 square feet. How many feet of fencing will she need for each side of her garden?

____

Name ______________________________

Guided Problem Solving
2-8

GPS PROBLEM 19, STUDENT PAGE 105

A Russian cosmonaut spent 439 days in space, returning to the earth in March of 1995.

a. How many hours did he spend in space? Write your answer in standard notation.

b. How many minutes did he spend in space? Write this answer in scientific notation.

Understand

1. What are you asked to do? ______________________________

____

Plan

2. How can you find how many hours are in

   a. 2 days? ______________ **b.** 439 days ______________

3. How can you find how many minutes are in

   a. 2 days? ______________ **b.** 439 days ______________

Solve

4. How many hours did the cosmonaut spend in space? ______________

5. How many minutes did the cosmonaut spend in space? ______________

6. Write the number of minutes in scientific notation. ______________

Look Back

7. Why did you write the number of minutes in standard notation before writing it in scientific notation?

____

____

____

SOLVE ANOTHER PROBLEM

Kate's birthday is February 29. She was born in a leap year.

a. How many days does she have to wait between birthdays? Write this answer in standard notation. ______________

b. How many minutes does she have to wait between birthdays? Write this answer in scientific notation. ______________

Name ______________________

Guided Problem Solving
2-9

PROBLEM 23, STUDENT PAGE 110

Arrange each of the following numbers from greatest to least. Explain your answer.

a. 1.24×10^{-3} **b.** 2.24×10^{-2} **c.** 1.89×10^{-4} **d.** -2.6×10^{-2}

Understand

1. Are these numbers written in standard or scientific notation? ______________

Plan

2. How can you tell whether a number written in scientific notation is negative?

____

____

3. Compare 10^{-4} and 10^{-3}. Which number is greater? ______________

4. How can you use an exponent to compare a power of ten?

____

____

5. Compare 1.6×10^{-2} and 2.6×10^{-2}. Which number is greater? ______________

6. When exponents are the same and neither of the other factors is negative, how can you compare the numbers?

____

Solve

7. Use your insights from Items 2, 4, and 6 to order the numbers.

____

Look Back

8. How could you have found the answer using a different method?

____

SOLVE ANOTHER PROBLEM

Arrange these numbers from least to greatest. Explain your answer.

a. 1.9×10^{-3} **b.** 2.5×10^{-4} **c.** 1.2×10^{-2} **d.** -2.8×10^{-4}

____

Name ____________________

Guided Problem Solving
3-1

GPS PROBLEM 13, STUDENT PAGE 125

Charles Lindbergh was the first person to fly nonstop solo across the Atlantic. In 1927 he flew from New York to Paris, a distance of 3610 miles, in 33.5 hours. What was his average speed?

Understand

1. What are you asked to find? ________

   a. distance **b.** average speed **c.** time

2. What are the given values? ____________________

Plan

3. Which formula should you use? ________

   a. $d = rt$ **b.** $r = \frac{d}{t}$ **c.** $t = \frac{d}{r}$

4. Which is a reasonable estimate of the average speed? ________

   a. about 100 mi/hr **b.** about 50 mi/hr **c.** about 200 mi/hr

Solve

5. Write the formula substituting the given values for the variables.

   ____

6. Solve the formula. Round your answer to the nearest tenth.

   ____

7. Write a sentence giving your answer to the problem.

   ____

Look Back

8. Is your answer reasonable? Explain.

   ____

   ____

SOLVE ANOTHER PROBLEM

The Kraeger family drove from Illinois to Florida on vacation. They drove a distance of 1158 miles in 21.5 hours. What was their average speed rounded to the nearest tenth of a mile? ____________________

Name ______________________________

Guided Problem Solving
3-2

GPS PROBLEM 19, STUDENT PAGE 130

When a tournament with n teams is held, the number of games needed for each team to play every other team is found using the expression $\frac{n \cdot (n - 1)}{2}$, where n is the number of teams. If there are 12 teams in a league, how many games are needed?

Understand

1. What are you asked to find? ______________________________

____

____

2. Write the expression you will use to find the answer. ______________

3. What does n represent in the expression? ________

   a. Number of teams b. Number of games

Plan

4. Which expression represents the number of games? ________

   a. $\frac{12 \cdot (12 - 1)}{2}$ b. $\frac{12 \cdot (12 - 1)}{12}$ c. $\frac{2 \cdot (12 - 1)}{2}$

Solve

5. Evaluate the expression. ______________

6. How many games are needed for 12 teams in a league? ______________

Look Back

7. What strategy could you use to see if your answer is reasonable?

____

SOLVE ANOTHER PROBLEM

When a tournament with n teams is held, the number of games needed for each team to play every other team is found using the expression $\frac{n \cdot (n - 1)}{2}$, where n is the number of teams. If there are 16 teams in a league, how many games are needed?

____

Name ______________________________

Guided Problem Solving 3-3

GPS PROBLEM 16, STUDENT PAGE 135

If a plane travels d miles and fuel is consumed at m miles per gallon, then its total fuel consumption g is obtained by dividing d by m.

a. Write a formula to describe the situation.

b. A Concorde can have a fuel consumption rate as low as 0.2 miles per gallon. How many gallons of fuel would the Concorde use on a flight from Paris to New York, a distance of 3600 miles?

Understand

1. What is the fuel consumption rate for a Concorde? ______________

2. How many miles is the distance from Paris to New York? ______________

3. What does each variable represent? ______________

____

Plan

4. Write the formula to describe total fuel consumption. ______________

Solve

5. Substitute the given values into the formula and solve for g. ______________

____

6. How many gallons of fuel does the Concorde use on a flight from Paris to New York? ______________

Look Back

7. How can you solve the problem using a different strategy? ______________

____

____

____

____

SOLVE ANOTHER PROBLEM

An auto has a fuel consumption rate of 30 miles per gallon. How many gallons of fuel would the auto use on a trip from Illinois to Florida, a distance of 1158 miles? ______________

Name ______________________________

Guided Problem Solving
3-4

GPS PROBLEM 23, STUDENT PAGE 143

A three-way light bulb has three different wattages available as you turn the switch three times in the same direction. The highest wattage is obtained by adding the two lower wattages. If the lowest wattage is 30 watts and the highest wattage is 100 watts, find the middle wattage.

Understand

1. What is the highest wattage? The lowest wattage? ______________

2. How is the highest wattage obtained? ______________

____

____

Plan

3. Which of the following would be a range within which the answer falls? ______

   a. Between 0-30 watts b. Between 130-200 watts

   c. Between 30 and 100 watts

4. Let w represent the middle wattage.
   Then choose the equation that best represents the situation. ______

   a. $w = 100 + 30$ b. $w + 30 = 100$ c. $w - 100 = 30$

Solve

6. Solve your chosen equation. ______________

7. What is the middle wattage? ______________

Look Back

8. How do you know your answer is reasonable? ______________

____

____

____

SOLVE ANOTHER PROBLEM

The highest wattage on a three-way light bulb is obtained by adding the two lower wattages. If the lowest wattage is 50 watts and the highest wattage is 250 watts, find the middle wattage. ______________

Name ______________________

Guided Problem Solving 3-5

GPS PROBLEM 30, STUDENT PAGE 149

An appliance that uses 1000 watts of power in 1 hour uses 1 kilowatt-hour (1 kWh) of energy. (Note that *kilo* means 1000.) Most electric companies charge by the kilowatt-hour. An appliance that uses 200 watts per hour for 5 hours also uses 1 kilowatt-hour of energy. Suppose a family uses 500 kWh in one month and they are charged $45. What is the cost per kWh?

Understand

1. How many kilowatt-hours were used in a month? ______________

2. How much was the family charged for the month? ______

3. What are you asked to find? ______________

Plan

4. Let c represent the cost per kWh. Then choose the equation that represents the situation. ______

   a. $500c = 45$ **b.** $45c = 500$ **c.** $c + 45 = 500$

5. Describe how you can isolate the variable and solve the equation.

____

____

Solve

6. Solve the equation you chose in Item 4. $c =$ ______

7. Write a sentence to give the cost per kWh.

____

____

Look Back

8. How can you check your answer? ______________

____

____

SOLVE ANOTHER PROBLEM

A family's electric bill one month showed 1400 kWh were used. The total charges were $196. What was the cost per kWh? ______

Name ____________________

Guided Problem Solving
3-6

PROBLEM 30, STUDENT PAGE 154

A paging service charges $20.00 for activation plus $12.95 a month. Francine paid $123.60 for activation and service. How many months did this cover?

Understand

1. How much does the paging service charge per month? __________

2. How much was the activation fee? __________

3. How much did Francine pay for activation and service? __________

Plan

4. Let *m* represent the number of months covered by $123.60. Then choose the equation that represents the situation. ________

   a. $20m = 123.60$ **b.** $12.95 + m = 123.60$ **c.** $20 + 12.95m = 123.60$

5. Which operation will you undo first? ________

   a. Multiplication **b.** Subtraction **c.** Addition

Solve

7. Solve the equation you chose in Item 4. __________

8. Write a sentence to give the final answer.

____

____

____

Look Back

9. How can you determine if your answer is reasonable?

____

____

____

SOLVE ANOTHER PROBLEM

Parking garage fees are $3 plus $1.50 per hour. If the total parking fee was $16.50, how many hours was the car parked? __________

Name ______________________________

Guided Problem Solving 3-7

GPS PROBLEM 30, STUDENT PAGE 159

You have made scores of 75 and 82 on your first two tests in Spanish. What scores can you get on your next test if you want to maintain an average of at least 80?

Understand

1. Circle the test scores you have already made.
2. What average do you want to maintain? ______________

Plan

3. Which operations do you use to find an average? ______

   a. Addition, subtraction **b.** Addition, division **c.** Multiplication, division

4. Let x represent the score on your next test. Which inequality represents the average of the test scores? ______

   a. $\frac{x + 75 + 82}{3} > 80$ **b.** $\frac{x + 75 + 82}{3} \geq 80$ **c.** $\frac{x + 75 + 82}{3} \leq 80$

Solve

5. Solve the inequality chosen in Item 4. __________
6. What score can you get on your next test to maintain an average of at least 80?

____

Look Back

7. You know that 75 is 5 less than the desired average and 82 is 2 greater than the desired average. How can this help you find the scores you need to get on your next test using mental math?

SOLVE ANOTHER PROBLEM

Your quiz scores are 85 and 91 in Social Studies. If you want to maintain an average of at least 90, what scores can you get on your next quiz?

____

Name ______________________________

Guided Problem Solving
4-1

PROBLEM 22, STUDENT PAGE 176

a. Draw the next figure.

b. What rule relates *n*, the figure number, to *d*, the number of dark tiles?

c. What rule relates *n* to *c*, the number of light tiles?

d. What rule relates *n* to *t*, the total number of tiles in each figure?

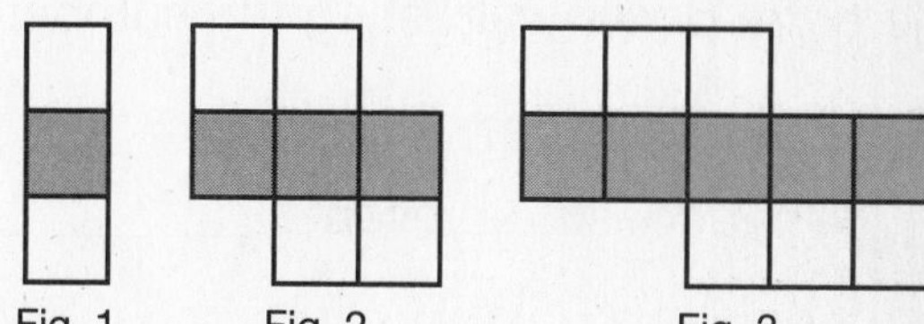

Understand

1. Circle each variable and what it represents.

Plan

2. Study the three given figures. Describe the pattern of dark tiles and the pattern of light tiles. Then tell how many of each will be in Figure 4.

____

____

____

Solve

3. Draw Figure 4.

4. Describe the rule relating the figure number to dark, light, or total tiles.

a. *n* to *d*. ____________ **b.** *n* to *c*. ____________ **c.** n to *t*. ____________

Look Back

5. Does Figure 4 follow the patterns you described in Items 2 and 3? ____________

SOLVE ANOTHER PROBLEM

Tell which rule relates *n* to *d* (figure number to dark tiles), *n* to *c* (figure number to light tiles), and *n* to *t* (figure number to total number of tiles) for this figure.

____

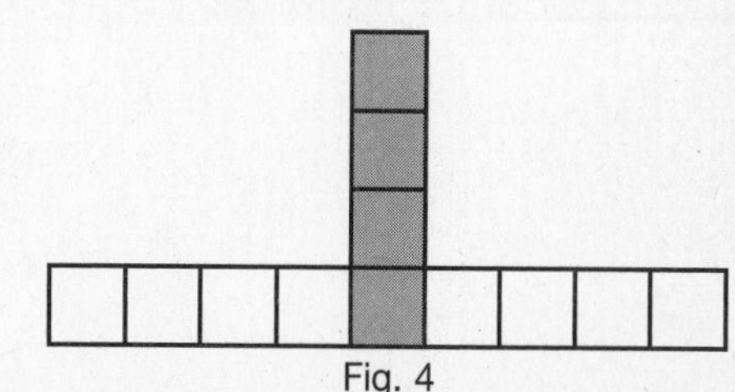
Fig. 4

Name ______________________________

Guided Problem Solving
4-2

GPS PROBLEM 19, STUDENT PAGE 180

The equation $y = 0.75t + 7.50$ represents the cost of a large pizza at Libonatti's, where t is the number of toppings. Make a table for the pizza parlor wall listing the number of toppings and the price.

Understand

1. What does t represent? ______________

2. What is the cost for each topping? ______________

3. What does 7.50 represent? ______________

Plan

4. Other than zero, what is the least value you can use for t? ______________

5. Why will you probably not use a value greater than 6 for t? ______________

____

Solve

6. Substitute 1 into the equation to find the cost for 1 topping, 2 for 2 toppings, 3 for 3 toppings, and so on. Then complete the table showing the cost of pizzas.

Number of toppings	0	1	2	3	4	5	6
Cost of large pizza	$7.50						

Look Back

7. What pattern can you find in the costs of the pizzas? ______________

____

SOLVE ANOTHER PROBLEM

The equation $y = 2.25g + 1.50$ represents the cost of bowling and shoe rental at the local bowling alley, where g represents the number of games bowled. Make a table for the bowling-alley wall listing the total cost of shoe rental and bowling up to 5 games.

Name ______________________

Guided Problem Solving
4-3

GPS PROBLEM 15, STUDENT PAGE 185

Jared has a coupon for \$2.00 off any order. He decides to buy bulk cat food for Nemo that sells for \$0.50 per pound. Use x for the number of pounds of cat food he will buy. Graph the price he will pay. What part of the graph does not make sense for the situation?

Understand

1. Circle the amount of the coupon. Will it be added to or subtracted from the price? ______________

Plan

2. Let x represent the number of pounds of cat food. Write an expression showing the cost at \$0.50 per pound. ______________

3. Write an expression for the cost of the cat food if the coupon is used. ______________

4. Make a table of values for the equation $y = 0.50x - 2$.

x	2	4	6	8
y				

Solve

5. On the grid, graph the ordered pairs from the table. Connect the points with a line.

6. What part of the graph does not make sense for the situation?

____

____

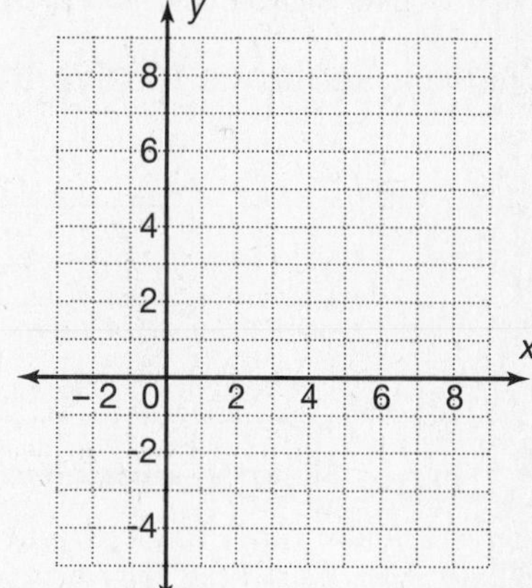

Look Back

7. What would it mean if the cost were negative? Is this reasonable?

____

SOLVE ANOTHER PROBLEM

Patty has a \$3 discount coupon off on any order. She buys bulk dog food for \$0.75 per pound. Use x for the number of pounds of dog food she will buy. On the grid above, graph the price she will pay. What part of the graph does not make sense for the situation?

____

Name ______________________________

Guided Problem Solving
4-4

GPS PROBLEM 15, STUDENT PAGE 193

A wheelchair ramp is allowed a maximum of one inch of rise for every foot of run. Express this slope as a fraction. (Hint: Use the same units.)

Understand

1. What is the rise? ______________________

2. What is the run? ______________________

3. How are you to write the slope? ______________________

Plan

4. Choose the correct definition. The slope is ______

   a. rise divided by the run. **b.** run divided by the rise.

5. If you express each measure in inches, what will you use for the rise and run?

   a. Rise __________ **b.** Run __________

Solve

6. Write the slope of the ramp. __________

7. Write a sentence to give the final answer.

____

____

____

Look Back

8. How can you find the answer using feet as the unit of measure?

____

SOLVE ANOTHER PROBLEM

A boat ramp has no more than four inches of rise for every three feet of run. Express this slope as a fraction. (Hint: Use the same units.)

____

Name ____________________

Guided Problem Solving 4-5

GPS PROBLEM 19, STUDENT PAGE 199

Marty belongs to a swim club. With a membership fee of \$20 per year, the members can swim any number of times for a reduced rate of \$2 per swim. Make a graph to show the total cost for varying numbers of swims. Explain how to find a typical cost from the graph.

Understand

1. How much is the membership fee? ____________

2. How much does it cost each time Marty swims? ________

Plan

3. Write an equation. Let x = the number of times Marty swims and y = the total cost. ____________

4. Make a table of ordered pairs for x and y.

x				
y	22	24	26	28

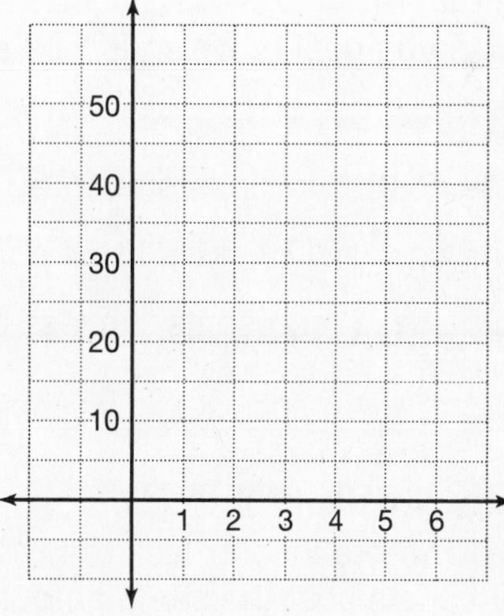

Solve

5. Graph the points on the grid.

6. Explain how to find a typical cost from the graph.

____

____

Look Back

7. What part of the graph does not make sense for the situation?

____

SOLVE ANOTHER PROBLEM

John pays \$35 each year for a zoo membership. As a member, he pays only a \$3 parking fee each time he visits the zoo. On the grid above, graph the total cost for varying numbers of zoo visits.

Name ______________________________

Guided Problem Solving
4-6

GPS PROBLEM 15, STUDENT PAGE 205

Which would be less expensive for 12 tickets, buying a weekend ski lift pass for $30.00 plus $1.50 per lift or just paying $4.00 per lift?

Understand

1. How many tickets will be purchased? ____________

2. How many different choices are there for buying the tickets? ____________

Plan

3. How can you find the cost of 12 tickets at $1.50 each plus $30 for a pass?

____

4. How can you find the cost of 12 tickets at $4 each? ____________

5. How can you decide which is less expensive? ____________

Solve

6. Find the cost of 12 tickets at $1.50 each plus $30 for a pass. ____________

7. Find the cost of 12 tickets at $4 each. ____________

8. Which method represents the less expensive way to buy 12 tickets?

____

Look Back

9. If you buy more than or less than 12 tickets, will both ways to buy tickets cost the same amount of money? Explain.

____

____

____

SOLVE ANOTHER PROBLEM

Which would be less expensive for 15 games at the carnival, paying an admission of $5 plus $1.50 for each game or buying game tokens for $2 each?

____

____

Name ______________________________

Guided Problem Solving
4-7

GPS PROBLEM 19, STUDENT PAGE 209

The Environment Club will have a party if the students collect at least 3.5 pounds of recyclable aluminum cans per student within a month. Graph the number of pounds (P) that must be collected by n students.

Understand

1. What is the least number of pounds of aluminum cans that needs to be collected per student? ____________

2. What does the variable P stand for? ____________

3. What does the variable n stand for? ____________

Plan

4. Write an equation using the variables. ____________

5. Since students can collect as much as or more than 3.5 pounds of cans per student, write an inequality using $\geq$. ____________

6. Make a table of values for $P = 3.5n$.

n				
P				

Solve

7. Use a solid line to graph the equation $P = 3.5n$.

8. Choose a point not on the line and substitute the ordered pair into the inequality. Shade one section of the graph.

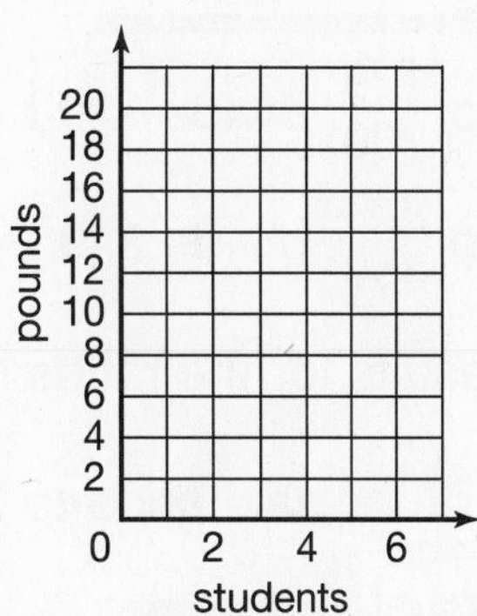

Look Back

9. How can you tell if you shaded the correct section on your graph? Explain.

____

____

SOLVE ANOTHER PROBLEM

The scout troop will go camping if the troop sells at least 12 boxes of cookies per scout. On another sheet of paper, graph the number of boxes (B) that must be sold by x scouts.

Name ________________________________

Guided Problem Solving 5-1

GPS PROBLEM 5, STUDENT PAGE 225

A modem originally priced at $200 is on sale for $129. A faster modem priced at $350 is on sale for $249. Is the ratio of the sale price to the original price the same?

Understand

1. How many modems are on sale? ________________

2. What ratio do you need to find for each modem?

____

Plan

3. Write the ratio for the first modem. ____________

4. Write the ratio for the faster modem. ____________

5. How can you compare the ratios for each modem?

____

____

Solve

6. For the ratio $\frac{129}{200}$, divide 129 by 200. ________________

7. For the ratio $\frac{249}{350}$, divide 249 by 350. ________________

8. Compare results for the ratios in Items 6 and 7. Are they the same? ________

9. Is the ratio of the sale price to the original price the same? ________

Look Back

10. Describe how you can compare the ratios using fractions rather than decimals.

____

____

SOLVE ANOTHER PROBLEM

An office-supply catalog has 10 packs of computer diskettes selling for $7.99 with a list price of $18.00. The catalog also sells 25 packs of diskettes for $18.99 with a list price of $38.00. Is the ratio of the selling price to the list price the same? ________

Name ______________________________

Guided Problem Solving
5-2

GPS PROBLEM 16, STUDENT PAGE 231

If phone calls are 30¢ per minute and are billed in 6-sec (0.1 min) increments, make an equal ratio table with at least six entries.

Understand

1. What is the charge per minute? ______________

2. How many seconds are in each billed increment? ______________

3. What do you need to make? ______________

4. How many entries do you need to find for the table? ______________

Plan

5. What is the given ratio for the equal ratio table? ______________

6. What will you label the two rows of the equal ratio table?

____

7. How will you find equal ratios to the left of 30¢:1 min in the table?

____

8. How will you find equal ratios to the right of 30¢:1 min in the table?

____

Solve

9. Complete the table to find 6 ratios equal to 30¢:1 min.

Cost (¢)				30	60	90
Minutes	0.1	0.2	0.5	1		

Look Back

10. How can you be sure all the ratios are equal? ______________

SOLVE ANOTHER PROBLEM

One long-distance phone company offered a special weekend rate of 15¢ per minute. The billing was in 20-second ($\frac{1}{3}$ minute) increments. Make an equal ratio table with at least six entries.

Name ______________________

Guided Problem Solving
5-3

GPS PROBLEM 13, STUDENT PAGE 238

Make a graph of downloading times to show that downloading a 900K file in 6 min is the same rate as downloading a 225K file in 1.5 min.

Understand

1. Circle both rates.

2. What are you asked to make? ______________________

Plan

3. Which part of the ratio will you graph on the x-axis? ________

   a. The time in minutes   b. The size of the file

4. Name the ordered pairs. ______________________

Solve

5. Complete the graph. Label the x-axis with time in minutes and the y-axis with file size.

Look Back

6. Why does your graph show that the rates are the same? ______________________

____

SOLVE ANOTHER PROBLEM

Make a graph of ticket costs to show that $60 for 5 admission tickets is the same rate as $24 for 2 tickets.

Name ______________________________

Guided Problem Solving
5-4

GPS **PROBLEM 31, STUDENT PAGE 246**

The lengths of the sides of a triangle are in a ratio of 6:5:3. The triangle's perimeter is 56 cm. What is the length of each side?

Understand

1. What is the ratio of the lengths of the sides of the triangle? __________

2. What is the perimeter of the triangle? __________

3. What are you asked to find? __________

Plan

4. How do you find the perimeter of a triangle? __________

5. What is the sum of the given ratios? __________

6. Divide the perimeter by the sum of the ratios. __________

Solve

7. Multiply each number in the ratio by your answer in Item 6 to find the lengths of the sides.

____

8. Write a sentence that answers the question to the problem.

____

____

Look Back

9. What other strategies can you use to solve the problem?

____

____

SOLVE ANOTHER PROBLEM

The lengths of the sides of a triangle are in a ratio of 5:4:3. The triangle's perimeter is 84 cm. What is the length of each side?

____

____

Name ______________________

Guided Problem Solving
5-5

GPS PROBLEM 13, STUDENT PAGE 250

Which is the better buy: a 16-oz box of cereal for $3.49 or a 6-oz box of cereal for $1.25?

Understand

1. How many sizes of boxes are you comparing? ______________

2. What do you need to find for each box size? ______________

Plan

3. Write the ratio $\frac{\text{cost}}{\text{ounces}}$ for each box size. ______________

4. Do you multiply or divide to find the unit rate for each box? ______________

Solve

5. Find the unit rate for the 16-oz box of cereal. Round your answer to the nearest cent. ______________

6. Find the unit rate for the 6-oz box of cereal. Round your answer to the nearest cent. ______________

7. Write a sentence that tells which product is the better buy.

____

____

Look Back

8. How can you check your answer?

____

____

____

SOLVE ANOTHER PROBLEM

Which is the better buy: a 4.6-oz tube of toothpaste for $1.89 or a 6.4-oz tube for $2.29? Give the unit rates to support your answer.

____

____

____

Name ______________________________

Guided Problem Solving
5-6

GPS PROBLEM 4, STUDENT PAGE 254

In a movie, large sets are often created so that people appear to be smaller. If a 60-in. tall person appears next to a 96-in. high trash can, but the trash can appears to be 18 in. high in the film, how tall would the person appear to be?

Understand

1. What will the 60-inch tall person stand next to? ______________

2. How tall will the trash can appear in the film? ______________

3. Will the person be larger or smaller than the trash can in the film? ______________

4. What do you need to find? ______________

Plan

5. Which ratio compares the actual height of the person to actual height of the trash can? ________

   a. $\frac{60}{96}$ b. $\frac{96}{60}$ c. $\frac{60}{18}$

6. Let x represent the height of the person in the film. Which ratio compares the height of the person to the height of the trash can in the film? ________

   a. $\frac{18}{x}$ b. $\frac{x}{96}$ c. $\frac{x}{18}$

Solve

7. Write a proportion using the equal ratios representing the height of the person to the height of the trash can. ______________

8. Solve the proportion for x and give the answer. $x =$ ______________

Look Back

9. How can you check to see if your answer is correct?

____

____

____

SOLVE ANOTHER PROBLEM

A 48-inch child is sitting in a 84-inch chair. If the chair will appear to be 42 inches high in the film, how tall will the child appear to be? ______________

Name ______________________________

Guided Problem Solving
5-7

GPS PROBLEM 21, STUDENT PAGE 261

The average NBA player is approximately 6 ft 9 in. tall, and the basket is 10 ft high. The average eighth grader is 5 ft 5 in. tall. How much should the basket be lowered for the eighth graders to make the ratio of player height to basket height the same?

Understand

1. How tall is the average NBA player? ____________

2. How tall is the average 8th grader? ____________

3. Should the basket be raised or lowered for the eighth graders? ____________

Plan

4. Convert all measurements to inches. Use 1 foot = 12 inches.

   a. 6 ft 9 in. ________ **b.** 5 ft 5 in. ________ **c.** 10 ft ________

5. Write a ratio of the NBA player's height to the basket height. ________

6. Let x = the adjusted height of the basket for an eighth grader. Write a ratio of the height for an eighth grader to the adjusted basket height. ________

Solve

7. Write the ratios as a proportion and solve for x. ____________

8. To find how much the basket should be lowered, first subtract the value of x from 120. Then write a sentence answering the question.

   ____

   ____

Look Back

9. How can you estimate to see if your answer is reasonable?

   ____

   ____

SOLVE ANOTHER PROBLEM

Suppose the average male height is 5 ft 9 in. What should the height of the basket be to the nearest inch so that player height is proportional to basket height? ________

Name ______________________________

Guided Problem Solving
6-1

GPS PROBLEM 23, STUDENT PAGE 279

To make the color light brown, you mix 7 parts red, 2 parts yellow, and 1 part blue. What percent of the light-brown coloring is red? Yellow? Blue?

Understand

1. What are you asked to find? ______________________________

2. How many parts of the color light brown are

   a. red? __________ b. yellow? __________ c. blue? __________

Plan

3. If the parts of the color light brown are written as a fraction, what would

   a. the numerator represent? ______________________________

   b. the denominator represent? ______________________________

4. How many parts are there in all in the color light brown? __________

Solve

5. Write the number of red parts as a fraction. ________

6. Write an equivalent fraction with the denominator 100 for the number of red parts. ________

7. Write the percent of the color light brown that is red. ________

8. Repeat steps 5–7 to find the percent that is yellow. ______________________________

9. Repeat steps 5–7 to find the percent that is blue. ______________________________

Look Back

10. How could you have solved the problem in a different way? ______________________________

____

SOLVE ANOTHER PROBLEM

There are 10 sixth-graders, 15 seventh-graders, and 25 eighth-graders in the drama club. What percent of the club members are sixth-graders? seventh-graders? eighth-graders?

____

Name ______________________

Guided Problem Solving
6-2

PROBLEM 14, STUDENT PAGE 284

A bin contains 120 ears of white and yellow corn. Of these, 78 ears are yellow. What percent of the ears of corn are yellow? What percent are white?

Understand

1. How many ears of corn are in the bin? ________

2. How many of the ears of corn in the bin are yellow? ________

3. What are you asked to find? ________

Plan

4. What percent of the corn is made up of both the yellow and the white ears? ________

5. Which proportion will you use to find the percent of yellow ears? ________

   a. $\frac{x}{120} = \frac{78}{100}$ **b.** $\frac{100}{120} = \frac{78}{x}$ **c.** $\frac{78}{120} = \frac{x}{100}$

6. Which operation can you use to find the percent of white corn once you know what percent is yellow and the total percent? ________

Solve

7. Solve your proportion to find the percent of yellow corn. ________

8. What is the percent of white corn in the bin? ________

Look Back

9. Check your answer by writing, then solving, an equation to find the percent of *white* corn in the bin.

____

SOLVE ANOTHER PROBLEM

There are 475 students at Washington Middle School. On the day of the big game, 304 students wore school colors. What percent of the students wore school colors? What percent did not wear school colors?

____

Name ______________________

Guided Problem Solving
6-3

GPS PROBLEM 24, STUDENT PAGE 290

The average daily intake of calories is 2000. For a snack, Leandro had yogurt (250 calories) and a small bag of chips (160 calories). Approximately what percent of his total caloric intake did Leandro have at lunch?

Understand

1. How many calories does Leandro consume per day? ______________

2. How many calories were in the yogurt? ______________

3. How many calories were in the bag of chips? ______________

Plan

4. Complete the equation to find how many calories were in the snack.

   ________ + ________ = ________

5. Write the fraction that shows what part of Leandro's average daily caloric intake was consumed during his snack. ________

Solve

6. Choose compatible numbers and rewrite the fraction in Item 5. ________

7. Write the fraction in Item 6 in lowest terms. ________

8. About what percent of his daily calories is in Leandro's snack? ________

Look Back

9. How does your answer change if you round to estimate Leandro's caloric intake without compensating for rounding both numbers up?

   ____

   ____

SOLVE ANOTHER PROBLEM

Monica ate spaghetti and a salad for lunch. She had a total of 450 calories and 15 grams of fat in her meal. Each gram of fat has 9 calories. Approximately what percent of the calories for her lunch came from fat? ________

Name ______________________

Guided Problem Solving 6-4

GPS PROBLEM 20, STUDENT PAGE 299

Suppose you make \$20,000 a year and spend 25% of your salary on rent. If your salary increases 10% and your rent increases 5%, what percent of your salary will be spent on housing?

Understand

1. What is your salary? ______________
2. What percent of your salary is spent on rent? _______
3. What is the percent increase in salary? _______
4. What is the percent increase in rent? _______

Plan

5. Write an equation to find the rent expense *before* any salary or rent increases. ______________________
6. Which equation will you use to find your new salary? Let x equal your new salary. _______

   a. $x = (20{,}000 \times 100\%) \times 10\%$ **b.** $x = 20{,}000 \times (100\% + 10\%)$

Solve

7. What is your salary *after* the increase? ______________
8. What is your rent *before* the increase? ______________
9. What is your rent *after* the increase? ______________
10. Write the ratio of new rental cost to new salary. ______________
11. Write the ratio in Item 10 as a percent. Round to the nearest whole number percent. _______

Look Back

12. Write another equation you could use to find the increased salary.

____

SOLVE ANOTHER PROBLEM

Suppose you make \$30,000 a year and spend 20% of your salary on rent. If your salary increases 4% and your rent increases 9%, what percent of your salary will be spent on housing? ______________

Name ______________________________

Guided Problem Solving 6-5

GPS PROBLEM 18, STUDENT PAGE 304

Ellen needs to raise the price of a $10 item and lower the price of a $15 item so they are equal. But she can only enter percent increases and percent decreases in the pricing computer. Give an example of how she can do this.

Understand

1. Underline the current prices of the two items.

2. Will the two new prices be the same or different amounts? __________

Plan

3. What range will the new price fall between? ________

   a. $10 and $15 **b.** $15 and $20 **c.** $20 and $25

4. Choose a number that falls within the range you chose in Item 4. ________

5. Write an equation to find the percent change between $10 and the price you selected. ____________________

6. Write an equation to find the percent change between $15 and the price you selected. ____________________

Solve

7. What is the percent change between $10 and the new price? Give change as a percent increase or decrease. ____________________

8. What is the percent change between $15 and the new price? Give change as a percent increase or decrease. ____________________

Look Back

9. Could you have chosen a different price for the two items? Explain. ____________

____

SOLVE ANOTHER PROBLEM

Jon needs to lower the prices of a $20 item and a $25 item so they are equal. But he can only enter percent increases and percent decreases in the computer. Give an example of how he can do this. ____________

____

____

Name ______________________________

Guided Problem Solving
6-6

GPS PROBLEM 23, STUDENT PAGE 310

A store has increased its wholesale prices 60%. What is the greatest percent of discount it can offer during a sale without selling its products below cost?

Understand

1. What percent were the prices originally increased? ________

2. What are you asked to find? ______________________________

____

Plan

3. Will the discount be less than, more than, or equal to 60%? Explain. ________

____

____

4. Solve a simpler problem by giving one of the products a price. If the wholesale price is $10, what is the current retail price? ________

5. Write an equation to find the percent decrease between the current retail price in Item 4 and $10. ______________

Solve

6. Solve your equation in Item 5 to find the greatest percent of discount the store could give without taking a loss. ________

Look Back

7. Choose another number to check your answer. Was the percent change the same? ______________

____

____

SOLVE ANOTHER PROBLEM

A store has increased its wholesale prices 150%. What is the greatest percent of discount it can offer during a sale without selling its products below cost? ________

Name ______________________________

Guided Problem Solving
7-1

GPS PROBLEM 40, STUDENT PAGE 329

Solve this puzzle: "The number is greater than 500 and less than 550. The number is odd and is a multiple of 9 and the ones digit is 1. What is the number?"

Understand

1. What numbers will the mystery number fall between? ______________

2. The mystery number is a multiple of which number? ________

3. What is the ones digit in the mystery number? ________

Plan

4. Let x = the mystery number. Write an inequality that shows which numbers the mystery number falls between.

____

5. How can you use divisibility rules to determine if a number is a multiple of 9? ______________________________

____

Solve

6. List the numbers with a 1 in the ones place that would solve the inequality you wrote in Item 4.

____

7. Use divisibility rules to find which of the numbers in Item 6 is divisible by 9. ________

Look Back

8. Why could you ignore the clue that the mystery number is odd? ______________

____

____

SOLVE ANOTHER PROBLEM

Solve this puzzle: "The number is less than 475 but greater than 425. The number is a multiple of 3, 6, and 9 and the ones digit is 2. What is the number?" ________

Name ______________________________

Guided Problem Solving
7-2

GPS PROBLEM 36, STUDENT PAGE 334

Dr. Pascal studies the effects of light sources on house plants. The number of plants in each class are 24, 30, 36, and 42. He wants to subdivide the classes into groups of the same size for the research project. What is the largest group size that will work in all four classes?

Understand

1. Circle the number of plants in each of the four classes.
2. Are the groups to be the same size or different sizes? ______________

Plan

3. How can finding the GCF of the class sizes help you find the group size? ______________
____
____
4. Make a factor tree for the number of plants in each class.

24 30 36 42

Solve

5. What are the common factors for all four numbers? ______________
6. What is the largest group size for the four classes? ______________

Look Back

7. What is another way to find the GCF of a group of numbers? ______________
____

SOLVE ANOTHER PROBLEM

In another study, the number of plants in each class are 32, 40, 48, and 64. Dr. Pascal wants to subdivide the classes into groups of the same size. What is the largest group size that will work in all four classes? ______________

Name ______________________________

Guided Problem Solving
7-3

GPS PROBLEM 22, STUDENT PAGE 338

Suppose Earth and Mars were aligned with the sun. Earth completes its orbit in 365 days and Mars completes its orbit in 687 days (orbits rounded to the nearest Earth day). When do both planets return to these same positions in their orbits?

Understand

1. How many days does it take the Earth to complete an orbit? ______________

2. How many days does it take Mars to complete an orbit? ______________

Plan

3. How can finding the LCM of the days it takes each planet to make one orbit around the sun help you find the number of days until the planets are aligned again? ______________________________

____

____

4. Make a factor tree for each number. 365 687

Solve

5. What are the prime factors of 365 and 687? ______________________

6. What is the highest power of each prime factor? ______________________

7. When will the planets return to these same positions in their orbits?

____

Look Back

8. Why should you express your answer in years?

____

SOLVE ANOTHER PROBLEM

Suppose Earth and Venus were aligned with the sun. Earth completes its orbit in 365 days and Venus its in 225 days (orbits rounded to the nearest Earth day). How many days until the planets are aligned again?

____

Name ______________________________

Guided Problem Solving
7-4

GPS PROBLEM 23, STUDENT PAGE 348

Marine animals, like the porpoise and the sea cow, get oxygen by breathing air, not from the water through gills, as fish do. A sea cow can stay underwater for $\frac{9}{30}$ hour. A porpoise can be underwater for $\frac{1}{4}$ hour. Which marine mammal can stay underwater longer?

Understand

1. What are you asked to find? ______________________________

____

2. How long can a sea cow stay underwater? __________

3. How long can a porpoise stay underwater? __________

Plan

4. What do you need to do first in order to compare fractions with different denominators? ______________________________

____

5. What do you need to do next? ______________________________

6. What is the LCD of 4 and 30? ______

Solve

7. Rewrite $\frac{9}{30}$ and $\frac{1}{4}$ using the LCD. $\frac{9}{30}$ = ______ $\frac{1}{4}$ = ______

8. Which fraction is larger? __________

9. Which marine mammal can stay underwater longer? ______________________________

Look Back

10. How could you find the answer by writing each time as a decimal? __________

____

SOLVE ANOTHER PROBLEM

Ken practiced shooting basketball free throws for $\frac{1}{3}$ hour. Max practiced shooting free throws for $\frac{2}{5}$ hour. Who practiced shooting longer? __________

Name ________________________________

Guided Problem Solving
7-5

GPS PROBLEM 29, STUDENT PAGE 354

Ana's stock rose $\frac{3}{4}$ of a point Wednesday, rose $\frac{3}{8}$ of a point Thursday, and fell $1\frac{1}{4}$ points Friday. Write an algebraic expression for the situation and find the overall change in her stock for these three days.

Understand

1. Underline the number of points the stock rose.
2. Circle the number of points the stock fell.
3. What two things are you asked to do? ________________________________

____

Plan

4. Would a rising stock price be a positive or a negative number? ____________
5. Would a falling stock price be a positive or a negative number? ____________

Solve

6. Write an expression for the change in stock price.

____

7. Simplify your expression. ________
8. What is the overall change in stock price. ________________________________

Look Back

9. How could you have used a calculator to find the answer? Would this be easier? Explain. ________________________________

____

____

SOLVE ANOTHER PROBLEM

Joe's stock rose $\frac{5}{8}$ of a point Monday, fell $\frac{7}{8}$ of a point Tuesday, and fell $2\frac{1}{2}$ points Wednesday. Write an algebraic expression for the situation and find the overall change in his stock for these three days.

____

Name ______________________________

Guided Problem Solving
7-6

GPS PROBLEM 28, STUDENT PAGE 360

Some say that the average ratio of inches of snow to inches of water is 10 to 1. If the snow is equivalent to $2\frac{7}{8}$ inches of water, how many inches of snow are there? Explain your reasoning.

Understand

1. What are you asked to find? ______________________________

____

2. What is the average ratio of inches of snow to inches of water? __________

Plan

3. Write $2\frac{7}{8}$ as a decimal. __________
4. Let x represent inches of snow. Write a proportion for the problem using 10 to 1 and x. __________

Solve

5. Solve for x. __________
6. How many inches of snow is equivalent to $2\frac{7}{8}$ inches of water? __________
7. Explain your reasoning. ______________________________

____

____

Look Back

8. How could you have found the answer using an improper fraction? __________

____

SOLVE ANOTHER PROBLEM

The average ratio of inches of rain to inches of snow is 1 to 10. How many inches of rain is equivalent to $16\frac{1}{2}$ inches of snow? Explain your reasoning.

____

____

____

Name ______________________________

Guided Problem Solving
7-7

GPS PROBLEM 23, STUDENT PAGE 368

The formula $t = \frac{\sqrt{d}}{4}$ shows how to find the time (t), in seconds, that it takes a falling object to free-fall a given distance (d). Find the falling time for a skydiver to fall 900 feet before opening the parachute.

Understand

1. What does the t in the formula $t = \frac{\sqrt{d}}{4}$ stand for? ____________

2. What does the d in the formula $t = \frac{\sqrt{d}}{4}$ stand for? ____________

3. You are asked to find how long it takes to fall how many feet? ____________

Plan

4. What is the first step in solving the formula? ________

   a. Divide d by 4. b. Find the square root of d.

5. What is the second step in solving the formula? ____________

6. What number will you substitute in the formula? ____________

7. Which is a reasonable time? ________

   a. 900 seconds b. 30 seconds c. 8 seconds

Solve

8. Solve using the formula. ____________

9. How many seconds does it takes to free-fall 900 feet. ____________

Look Back

10. If your answer and your estimate are not close, how can you determine if your answer is reasonable? ____________

____

____

SOLVE ANOTHER PROBLEM

Find the falling time for a skydiver to fall 1600 feet before opening the parachute.

____

Name ______________________________

Guided Problem Solving 7-8

GPS PROBLEM 28, STUDENT PAGE 372

You can find the number of seconds that it takes a pendulum to swing back and forth. First, find the square root of the pendulum's length in meters, then double it. How long will it take a pendulum that is 1.2 meters long to swing back and forth?

Understand

1. What are you asked to find? ______________________________

____

2. What is the pendulum's length? ______________

3. Underline the steps to use in finding the number of seconds.

Plan

4. How can you find the square root of a number using a calculator? ______________

____

5. How would you double a number? ______________

Solve

6. Use a calculator to find the square root of 1.2. Round the answer to the nearest thousandth. __________

7. Double the square root of 1.2. __________

8. How long will it take a 1.2 meter pendulum to swing back and forth? ______________

Look Back

9. Why is it important to follow the steps in order? What happens if you switch the order? ______________

____

____

SOLVE ANOTHER PROBLEM

How long will it take a pendulum that is 9.6 meters long to swing back and forth?

____

Name ____________________

Guided Problem Solving
7-9

GPS **PROBLEM 15, STUDENT PAGE 378**

A square courtyard with a diagonal walkway has an area of 81 square feet.

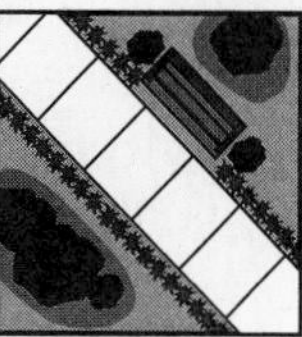

a. Find the length of the sides of the courtyard.

b. Find the length of the walkway.

Understand

1. What is the area of the square courtyard? ____________________

2. What figure is formed by two sides of the courtyard and the diagonal walkway? ____________________

3. What part of the figure named in Item 2 represents the longest part of the walkway? ____________________

Plan

4. How can you find the length of each courtyard side? ____________________

5. How can the Pythagorean Theorem help find the walkway length?

____

____

Solve

6. What is the length of each side of the courtyard? ____________

7. What is the length of the longest part of the walkway rounded to the nearest thousandth? ____________

Look Back

8. How can you check your answer? ____________________

____

____

____

SOLVE ANOTHER PROBLEM

A square courtyard with a diagonal walkway has an area of 324 ft^2. Find the length of

a. the sides of the courtyard. __________ **b.** the walkway. __________

Name ______________________________

Guided Problem Solving
8-1

GPS PROBLEM 15, STUDENT PAGE 394

For a geology experiment, a group of students measure the mass of a piece of copper. Their results were 15.64 g, 15.69 g, 15.67 g, 0.01566 kg, and 0.01564 kg. What is the average of the students' measurements?

Understand

1. What are you asked to find? ______________________________
2. Underline the measurements of the copper piece.

Plan

3. How do you find the average of a set of numbers? ______________________________

____

____

4. To convert from kilograms to grams, which ratio will you use? ________

a. $\frac{1000 \text{ g}}{1 \text{ kg}}$ b. $\frac{1 \text{ kg}}{1000 \text{ g}}$

Solve

5. Convert the measurements from kilograms to grams.

a. 0.01566 kg ____________ b. 0.01564 kg ____________

6. What is the sum of the measures in grams? ____________
7. What is the average mass? ____________

Look Back

8. How could you Work Backward to check your answer? ______________________________

____

____

SOLVE ANOTHER PROBLEM

For a math activity, a group of students measured the length of piece of string. Their results were 234.4 cm, 235 cm, 2.34 m, and 2.348 m. What is the average of the students' measurements? ____________

Name ______________________________

Guided Problem Solving
8-2

GPS PROBLEM 19, STUDENT PAGE 400

An Olympic marathon covers 42.2 km of distance through the streets of the host city, followed by a 400 m lap around the main stadium. What is the total distance of the race, in meters? Use significant digits.

Understand

1. What are you asked to find? ______________________________

2. What is the length of the part of the race through the streets? ____________

3. What is the length of the lap in the stadium? ____________

Plan

4. How many meters are in a kilometer? ____________

5. Convert 42.2 km to meters. ____________

6. Which operation will you use to find the total distance of the marathon? ____________

Solve

7. Write an equation to find the total distance of the marathon.

____

8. What is the total distance? ____________

9. What are the significant digits in the total distance? ____________

Look Back

10. What are two ways to convert 42.2 km to meters? ______________________________

____

____

SOLVE ANOTHER PROBLEM

A bicycle race covers 34.8 km over winding country roads and 500 m in the final straight stretch across the finish line. What is the total distance of the race, in meters? ____________

Name ____________________

Guided Problem Solving
8-3

GPS PROBLEM 16, STUDENT PAGE 406

The west coast of Cuba is at 85° W and the east coast of Cuba is at 74° W. If at that latitude, a 5° change in longitude represents about 300 mi, how far is it from coast to coast? Explain your answer.

Understand

1. What is the longitude at the west coast? ____________
2. What is the longitude at the east coast? ____________

Plan

4. Given the longitude, which operation will you use to find the distance across Cuba in degrees? ____________
5. How many miles is represented by a 1° change in longitude at that latitude? ____________
6. Which operation will you use to find the distance across Cuba in miles? ____________

Solve

7. How many degrees is it between the west and east coasts of Cuba? ____________
8. What is the distance in miles between the west and east coasts of Cuba? ____________
9. Explain your answer. ____________________

Look Back

10. Show how you could find the answer by writing and solving a proportion.

____

SOLVE ANOTHER PROBLEM

The west coast of Australia is at 113° E and the east coast of Australia is at 153° E. If at that latitude, a 10° change in longitude represents about 625 mi, how far is it from coast to coast? Explain your answer.

____

____

Name ______________________________

Guided Problem Solving
8-4

GPS PROBLEM 41, STUDENT PAGE 415

Two angles are supplementary. One angle measures x degrees, the other y degrees. Write an equation expressing that these angles are supplementary, and solve this equation for y. Find y if $x = 71°$.

Understand

1. What kind of angles are the two angles? ______________

2. What are the measures of the two angles? ______________

3. Underline what you are asked to do.

Plan

4. What does it mean that angles are supplementary?

____

5. Which is a reasonable measure for one of two supplementary angles if the other angle measures 71°? ______

   a. Less than 90°   **b.** Between 90° and 180°   **c.** Greater than 180°

Solve

6. Use the measures of the two angles to write an equation showing the sum of two supplementary angles. ______________

7. Solve the equation in Item 6 for y. ______________

8. Substitute 71 for x in the equation in Item 7. Solve for y. ______________

Look Back

9. Use a protractor to draw a 71° angle. Label it $\angle x$. Then draw the supplement of $\angle x$ and label it $\angle y$. Measure $\angle y$.

   ____

SOLVE ANOTHER PROBLEM

Two angles are complementary. One angle measures x degrees, the other y degrees. Write an equation expressing the fact that these angles are complementary, and solve this equation for y. Find y if $x = 29°$.

____

Name ______________________________

Guided Problem Solving
8-5

GPS PROBLEM 23, STUDENT PAGE 420

KP || *VF*. Find the measure of each numbered angle.

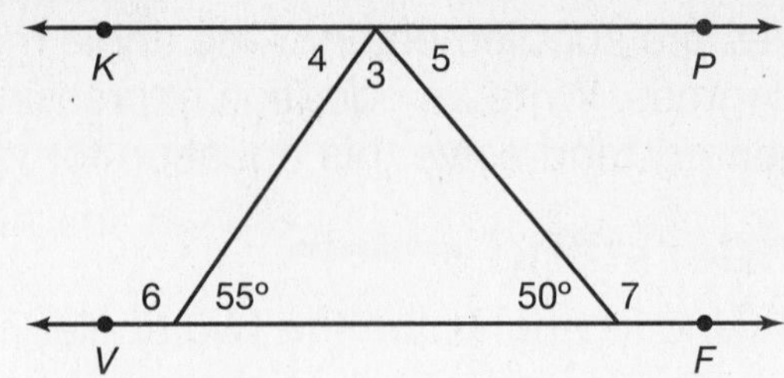

Understand

1. What polygon is shown in the diagram? __________
2. Two sides of the polygon intersect parallel lines. What are these lines called? ________

   a. Transversals **b.** Corresponding lines **c.** Perpendicular lines

Plan

3. What is the sum of the measures of the angles of a triangle? __________
4. What is true about the measures of alternate interior angles? __________
5. Name an alternate interior angle for the 55° angle. ______ The 50° angle. ______
6. What is true about the measures of supplementary angles? __________
7. Name an angle supplementary to the 55° angle. ______ The 50° angle. ______

Solve

8. Write the measure **a.** of ∠3. _______ **b.** of ∠4. _______

   c. of ∠5. _______ **d.** of ∠6. _______ **e.** of ∠7. _______

Look Back

9. What is another way to find the measure of ∠3? __________

____

SOLVE ANOTHER PROBLEM

AB || *CD*. Find the measure of each numbered angle.

____

____

____

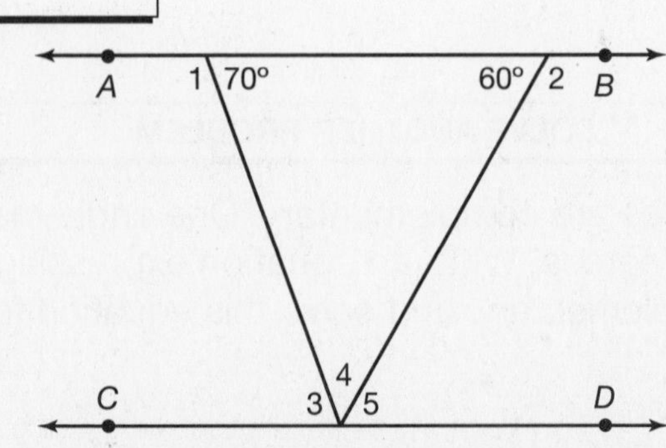

Name ______________________________

Guided Problem Solving
8-6

PROBLEM 25, STUDENT PAGE 426

Draw an isosceles triangle with side lengths of 4 in. and 7 in. Determine the length of the third side. Is this the only possible isosceles triangle that has the side lengths 4 in. and 7 in.? Explain.

Understand

1. What defines an isosceles triangle? ______________________________

Plan

2. If only *one* side measures 4 in., what will be the measures of the other two sides? ______________

3. If only *one* side measures 7 in., what will be the measures of the other two sides? ______________

4. Use a compass and a ruler to draw the triangle on another sheet of paper. Draw a segment. Set the compass to one of your measures. Place the compass on each endpoint and draw two intersecting arcs above it. Connect the three points.

Solve

5. Measure the sides. One side should measure 4 in. and another side should measure 7 in. What is the measure of the third side? ________

6. Repeat the procedure in Item 4 to draw different triangles. How many triangles can you draw? Explain. ______________________________

____

____

Look Back

7. How can you use the relationship between the measures of the sides of the angles in a triangle to determine whether or not you can draw an isosceles triangle with any given measures? ______________

____

SOLVE ANOTHER PROBLEM

Draw an isosceles triangle with side lengths of 2 cm and 5 cm. Determine the length of the third side. Is this the only possible isosceles triangle that has the side lengths 2 cm and 5 cm? Explain. ______________

____

Name ______________________________

Guided Problem Solving
8-7

PROBLEM 9, STUDENT PAGE 431

Which net matches the 3-D figure?

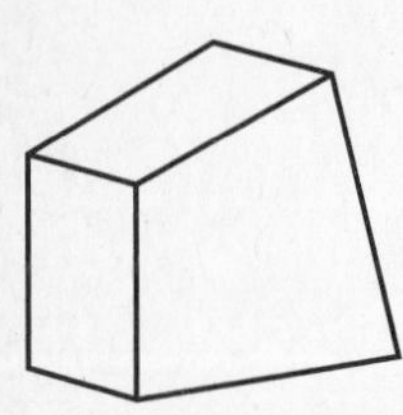

A

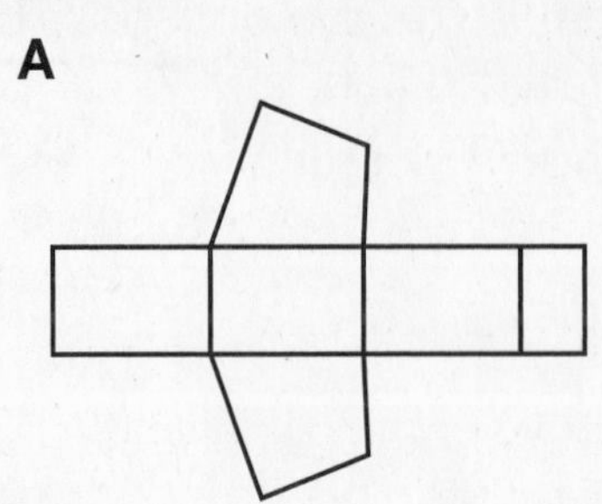

B

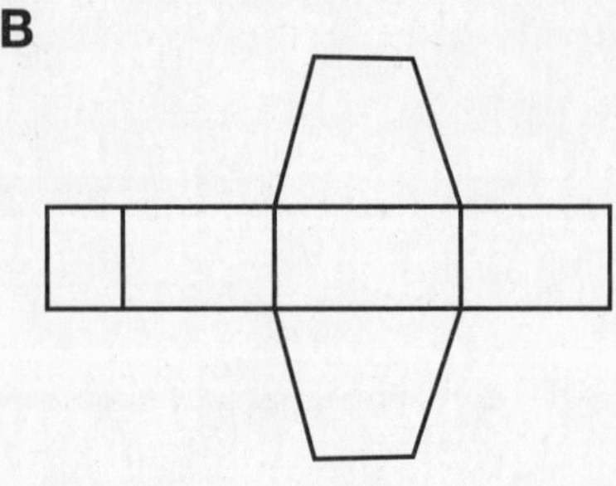

Understand

1. How many sides of the 3-D figure can you see? __________

2. Which polygons make up these sides? ______________________________

3. How many sides of each net can you see? __________

4. Which polygons make up these sides? ______________________________

Plan

5. How are the two nets alike? ______________________________

6. How do the nets differ? ______________________________

Solve

7. Choose one of the differences between the nets and compare that characteristic to the solid. Which net matches the solid? __________

Look Back

8. Which difference between the nets is the easiest to use to compare to the solid? Explain. ______________________________

____

SOLVE ANOTHER PROBLEM

Which net matches the 3-D figure? __________

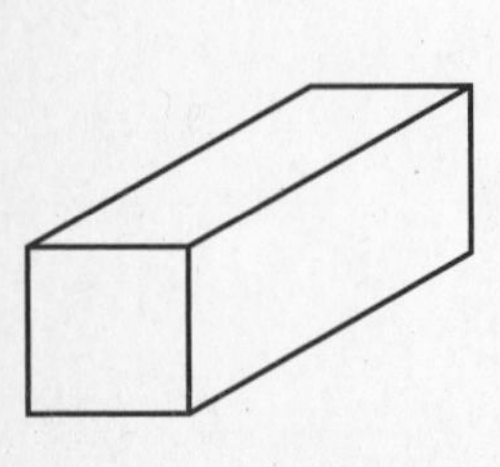

A

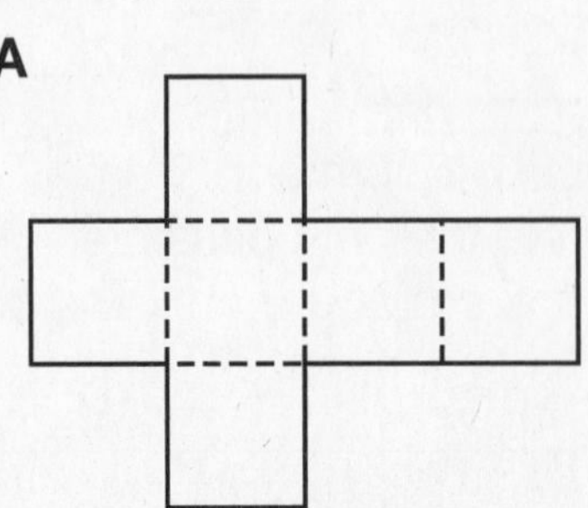

B

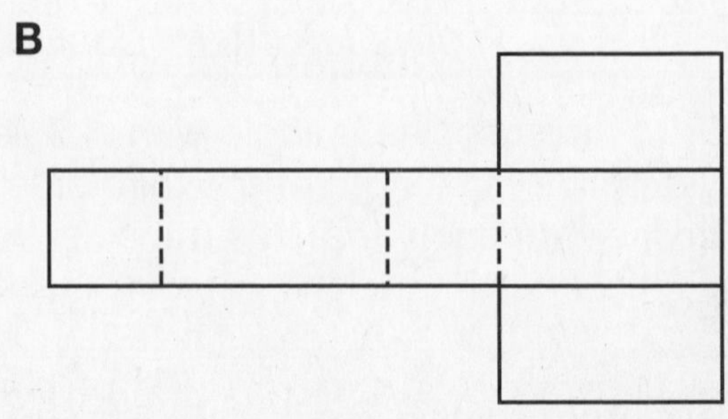

Name ______________________________

Guided Problem Solving
9-1

GPS PROBLEM 15, STUDENT PAGE 448

A set designer wants to make a parlor room 16 ft by 24 ft.

a. How much tape does he need to mark out the room on the stage?

b. How much carpet does he need to cover the whole floor?

Understand

1. What are the dimensions of the parlor room? ______________

2. Will the designer use the tape to mark the perimeter or the area of the room? ______________

3. Will the carpet cover the perimeter or area of the room? ______________

Plan

4. Draw a sketch of the room. Label each measure.

5. What is the formula for the perimeter of a rectangle? ______________

6. What is the formula for the area of a rectangle? ______________

7. What is a reasonable area for the room? ________

a. 80 ft^2 **b.** 160 ft^2 **c.** 200 ft^2 **d.** 400 ft^2

Solve

8. How much tape will be needed to mark out the room on the stage? ______________

9. How much carpet will be needed to cover the whole floor? ______________

Look Back

10. What is another way to find the perimeter? ______________

SOLVE ANOTHER PROBLEM

An interior designer is designing a room 21 ft by 28 ft.

a. How much wallpaper border does she need to place a strip at the top of the walls around the entire room? ______________

b. How much carpet does she need to cover the whole floor? ______________

Name ______________________________

Guided Problem Solving
9-2

GPS PROBLEM 8, STUDENT PAGE 454

A Shakespearean theater group wants to buy material for its new rectangular stage. On the model, the stage is 40 cm by 100 cm. The scale factor reads 25. What is the minimum length of a string of lights around the perimeter of the stage?

Understand

1. What figure is the stage? ______________

2. What are the model's dimensions? ______________

3. What is the scale factor? ________

Plan

4. What is the formula for the perimeter of a rectangle? ______________

5. How can you find the dimensions of the stage given the dimensions of the model and the scale factor?

____

Solve

6. One dimension of the model is 40 cm.
   What is this dimension of the actual stage? ______________

7. What is the other dimension of the actual stage? ______________

8. What is the minimum length of a string of lights around the perimeter of the stage? ______________

Look Back

9. What is another way to find the length of the lights? ______________

____

____

SOLVE ANOTHER PROBLEM

A model of a stage is 100 cm by 50 cm. The scale factor reads 20. What is the minimum length of raised trim that can be used around the perimeter of the stage? ______________

Name ______________________________

Guided Problem Solving
9-3

GPS PROBLEM 17, STUDENT PAGE 460

A theater owner wants to design a Greek style semicircular stage with a radius of 30 ft. Explain how to find the perimeter and area of the stage. Include an illustration.

Understand

1. Underline what you are asked to explain.

2. What figure is the stage? ______________

Plan

3. Draw the shape of the stage. Label the radius.

4. The area of the stage is what fraction of the area of a circle? ______

5. The curved part of the stage is what fraction of the circumference of a circle? ______

6. How can you find the measure of the straight part? ______________

Solve

7. Explain how to find the perimeter of the stage. ______________

____

8. Explain how to find the area of the stage. ______________

Look Back

9. Follow the steps in your explanations to find the area and perimeter of the stage. Write each measure. Are your explanations complete?

____

SOLVE ANOTHER PROBLEM

A stage has a semicircular section with a radius of 15 ft. A square with sides equal to the straight part of the semicircle extends from that part. Explain how to find the perimeter and area of the stage. Include an illustration.

____

____

____

Name ________________________________

Guided Problem Solving
9-4

GPS PROBLEM 15, STUDENT PAGE 465

A cereal company is making a jumbo-size box by doubling the dimensions of its midsize box which is 12 in. by 8 in. by 2 in. How much more cardboard will be needed to make the jumbo size?

Understand

1. What are the dimensions of the midsize box? ________________
2. How many times greater are the dimensions of the jumbo-size box than the midsize box? ________________

Plan

3. What are the dimensions of the jumbo-size box? ________________
4. How do you find the surface area of the box? ________________
5. Draw and label a net for each box size.

Solve

6. How much cardboard is needed to make the midsize box? ________________
7. How much cardboard is needed to make the jumbo-size box? ________________
8. How many more square inches of cardboard is needed to make the jumbo-size box than to make the midsize box? ________________

Look Back

9. How does the relationship between the dimensions and surface areas of the two boxes compare to the relationship between the dimensions and area of a dilated rectangle with a scale factor of 2? ________________

____

SOLVE ANOTHER PROBLEM

A company is making a regular-size cracker box by tripling the dimensions of its sample box which is 4 in. by 3 in. by 1 in. How much more cardboard will be needed to make the regular size? ________________

Name ______________________

Guided Problem Solving
9-5

GPS PROBLEM 9, STUDENT PAGE 471

Sioux tepees are cone-shaped. If the diameter of a tepee is 18 ft and the height is 12 ft, how much buffalo hide is needed to cover the outside surface?

Understand

1. Underline the diameter and height of the tepee.

2. What shape is the tepee? ______________

3. Is the floor area inside the tepee covered with buffalo hide? ______

Plan

4. What is the radius of the tepee? ______

5. Which formula you will use to find the area of the curved surface? ______

   a. $A = \frac{1}{2}Cs$ b. $A = \pi r^2$ c. $A = Csr^2$

6. What kind of triangle is formed by the slant height, radius, and height of a cone? ______________

7. Which theorem can you use to find the measure of the slant height? ______________

Solve

8. What is the slant height of the cone? ______

9. Write an equation to show how to find how much buffalo hide is needed.

   ____

10. How much buffalo hide is needed to cover the outside surface? ____________

Look Back

11. Why isn't the area of the opening subtracted to find the amount of buffalo skin needed? ______________

    ____

SOLVE ANOTHER PROBLEM

A campsite has platform shelters shaped like cones. If the height of each shelter is 12 feet and the diameter is 10 ft, how much canvas is needed to cover the outside of each shelter ____________

Name ______________________________

Guided Problem Solving 9-6

GPS PROBLEM 9, STUDENT PAGE 479

Sketch the figure. Then find the volume of a fly-casting pool in the park that is 30 ft wide, 40 ft long, and 5 ft deep.

Understand

1. What are you asked to find? ______________________

2. What figure is the pond? ______________________

3. What is each dimension of the pool?

   a. Width ________ b. Length ________ c. Depth ________

Plan

4. Sketch the figure for the pond. Label each dimension.

5. How can you find the volume of the pond? ______________________

   ____

6. How can you find the area of the bottom of the pool? ______________________

   ____

Solve

7. What is the area of the bottom of the pool? ____________

8. What is the volume of the pool? ____________

Look Back

9. How could you find the volume without drawing a sketch? ______________________

   ____

SOLVE ANOTHER PROBLEM

Sketch the figure. Then find the volume of a fish pond at the zoo that is 20 ft wide, 25 ft long, and 3 ft deep.

____

Name ______________________________

Guided Problem Solving
9-7

GPS PROBLEM 13, STUDENT PAGE 486

You have a package 24 in. by 18 in. by 12 in. to ship. E-Z Shipping charges by volume \$0.002 per in^3 whereas Speedy Shipping charges by surface area \$0.005 per in^2.

a. Which company is cheaper for this package?

b. Will this be true for all shapes of packages? Explain.

Understand

1. Underline the dimensions of the package.
2. Circle each company's rate.

Plan

3. What formula can you use to find the volume of the package? ____________
4. Sketch the net for the package.
5. What formula can you use to find the area of each face? ____________
6. Which operation will you use to find the cost? ________________

Solve

7. Find the volume of the package. ____________ The surface area. ____________
8. What is the shipping cost for each company?

   a. E-Z Shipping ____________ **b.** Speedy Shipping ____________

9. Which company is cheaper for this package? ____________________
10. Will this be true for all shapes of packages? Explain. ____________________

    ____

Look Back

11. Would calculations be easier if rates and measurements were converted to feet before multiplying? Explain. ____________

    ____

SOLVE ANOTHER PROBLEM

Use the rates above. Is it cheaper to ship a package measuring 12 in. by 20 in. by 4 in. using E-Z Shipping or Speedy Shipping? ____________

Name ______________________________

Guided Problem Solving
9-8

PROBLEM 11, STUDENT PAGE 491

Find the volume of the shaded region in the figure.

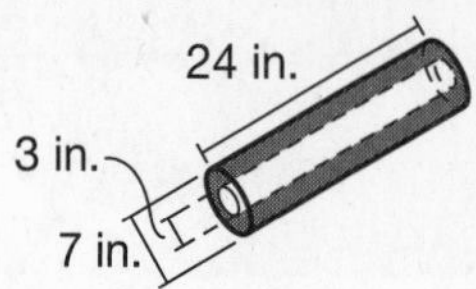

Understand

1. Which two solids make up the figure? ____________

2. What is the diameter of the inside figure? ______ The outside figure? ______

3. What is the height of both figures? ______

Plan

4. What is the radius of the inside figure? ______ The outside figure? ______

5. What is the formula for finding the volume of a cylinder? __________

6. What is the formula for finding the area of the flat part of a cylinder?

____

7. How can you find the volume of the shaded region? ____________________

____

Solve

8. What is the volume of the outside cylinder? ____________

9. What is the volume of the inside cylinder? ____________

10. What is the volume of the shaded region? ____________

Look Back

11. What is another way to find the volume of the shaded space? ____________

____

SOLVE ANOTHER PROBLEM

Find the volume of the shaded region in the figure.

____

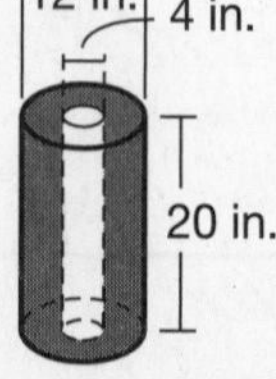

Name ______________________________

Guided Problem Solving
9-9

PROBLEM 13, STUDENT PAGE 496

Which solid has a greater volume, the pyramid or cone?

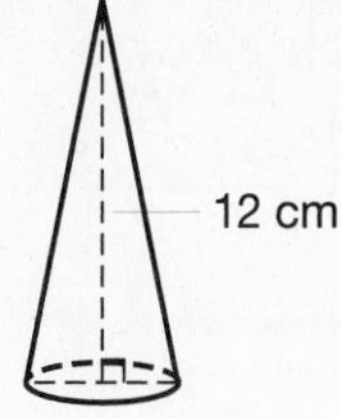

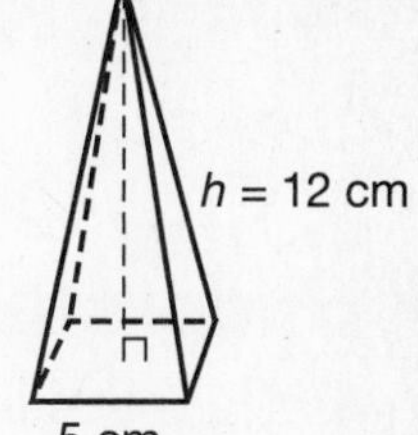

Understand

1. What is the height of the cone? __________

2. What is the height of the pyramid? __________

Plan

3. What is the formula for finding the volume of a cone? __________

4. What is the formula for finding the base of the cone? __________

5. What is the formula for finding the volume of a pyramid? __________

6. What is the formula for finding the base of the pyramid? __________

Solve

7. What is the volume of the cone? __________

8. What is the volume of the pyramid? __________

9. Which solid has the greater volume? __________

Look Back

10. How could you find the greater volume without actually calculating the volume of each figure? Explain. __________

____

____

____

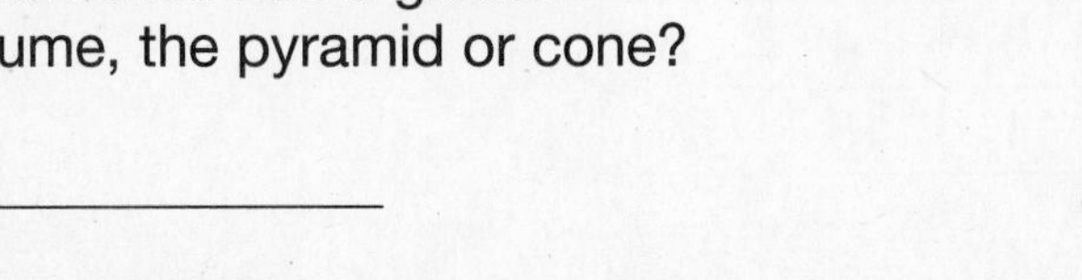

SOLVE ANOTHER PROBLEM

Which solid has a greater volume, the pyramid or cone?

____

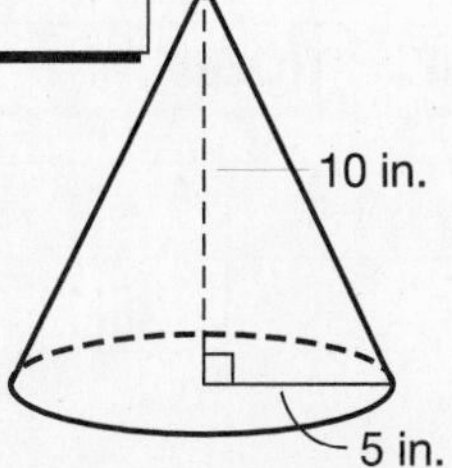

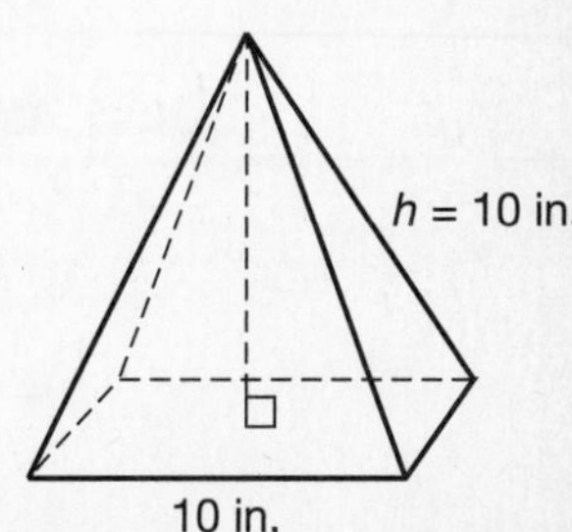

Name ____________________

Guided Problem Solving
10-1

 **PROBLEM 20, STUDENT PAGE 512**

Guess my rule.

If you say...	3	5	6	10
I say...	8	24	35	99

Understand

1. What are the input values? __________
2. What are the output values? __________
3. Is the relationship a function? ______

Plan

4. Can one of the following operations and a constant (the same number) be applied to each input value in the table to get each output value?

   a. Addition? ____ b. Subtraction? ____ c. Multiplication? ____

   d. Division? ____ e. Exponents (x^2, x^3...) ____

5. Which operation and constant when applied to the input value results in a number that is closest to the output value? ____
6. What do you need to do to your anwer to Item 5 to obtain the output value? ______

   a. Add 1. b. Subtract 1. c. Add 2.

Solve

7. What is the rule? ____________________

Look Back

8. How can you tell that you will need to multiply or use an exponent in the function? ____________________

____

SOLVE ANOTHER PROBLEM

Guess my rule.

If you say...	2	3	4	8
I say...	6	11	18	66

____

Name ______________________________

Guided Problem Solving 10-2

 **PROBLEM 11, STUDENT PAGE 516**

The distance the fastest marine animal, a killer whale, can travel is a function of the time traveled. The killer whale travels approximately 34.5 mi/hr.

a. Write an equation to show the relationship between distance and time.

b. Use your equation to find how far the whale can travel in 2 hr, 6 hr, and 10 hr.

Understand

1. Distance is part of the function. What is the other part? ______________

2. What is the rate (speed) that the whale travels? ______________

Plan

3. Which is the input value? ______________ The output value? ______________

4. Which equation shows the relationship between distance and time. ________

a. $d = r + t$ **b.** $d = rt$ **c.** $d = \frac{r}{t}$ **d.** $r = \frac{t}{d}$

Solve

5. Substitute the rate into the equation from Item 4 to show the relationship between distance and time traveled for the killer whale. ______________

6. Substitute into the equation you wrote in Item 5 to find the distance the killer whale travels in each time below.

a. 2 hr ______________ **b.** 6 hr ______________ **c.** 10 hr ______________

Look Back

7. What other strategy could you use to find the answer? ______________

SOLVE ANOTHER PROBLEM

The distance the largest whale, a blue whale, can travel is a function of the time traveled. A 90-foot blue whale, swimming at normal speed, moves approximately 16 mi/hr.

a. Write an equation to show the relationship between distance and time. ______________

b. Use your equation to find how far the whale can travel for each time.

2 hr ______________ 5 hr ______________ 8 hr ______________

Name ______________________________

Guided Problem Solving
10-3

GPS **PROBLEM 14, STUDENT PAGE 522**

A toy rocket was launched into the air. The function $h = 50t - 5t^2$ models this situation, where h = height in m and t = time in sec.

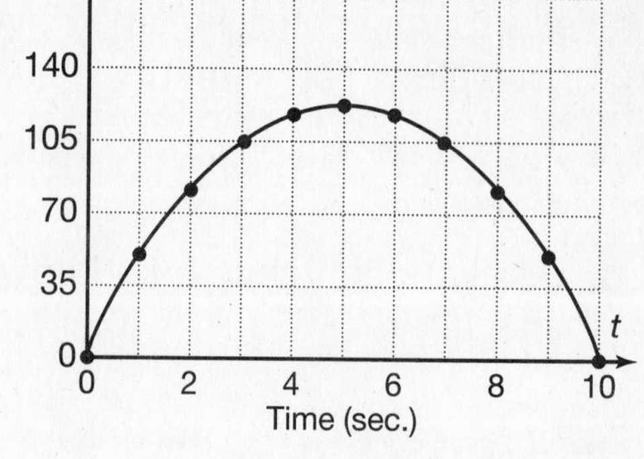

a. When is the rocket 105 m in the air? Explain.

b. What happens at 10 sec?

Understand

1. Circle the function.

2. Which axis in the graph represents height? ____________

Plan

3. Can there be more than one time for each height? Why? ____________

____

4. How can you find the values? ____________

Solve

5. When is the rocket 105 m in the air? What is happening at this time? ____________

____

6. What is the height at 10 sec? What is happening to the rocket?

____

Look Back

7. Why doesn't the graph extend below the x-axis? ____________

____

SOLVE ANOTHER PROBLEM

An object is launched into the air. The function $h = 80t - 16t^2$ models this situation, where h = height in ft and t = time in sec.

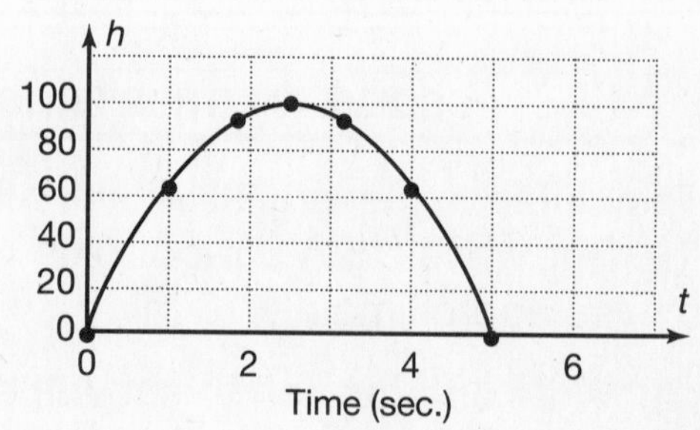

a. When is the object 64 feet in the air? Explain.

____

b. What happens at $2\frac{1}{2}$ sec? ____________

Name ____________________

Guided Problem Solving
10-4

PROBLEM 11, STUDENT PAGE 526

Ready Rent-All rental charges for a VCR are as follows.

Rental Time	Rental Fee
One day or portion thereof	$10.00
over 1 day, up to 3 days	$20.00
over 3 days, up to 5 days	$35.00

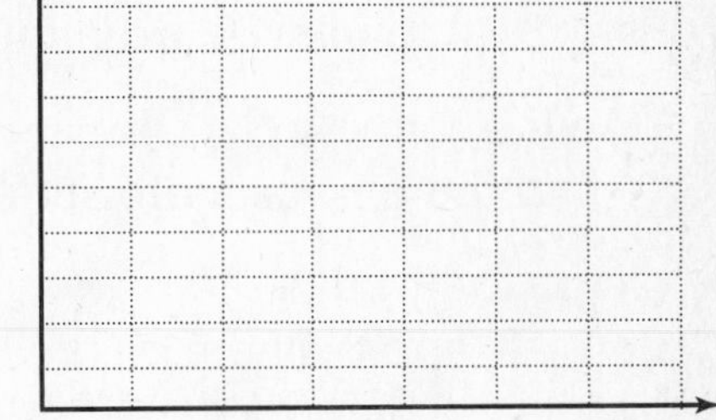

a. Graph the function.

b. What kind of function is this?

Understand

1. What is the fee for renting a VCR for each time period?

a. 0 hr ________ **b.** 5 hr ________ **c.** 23 hr ________ **d.** 25 hr ________

Plan

2. Which is the independent variable, time or rental fee? ____________

3. On which axis will you graph the number of days? ____________

Solve

4. Graph the function on the grid above.

5. What kind of function did you graph? ________

a. Step function **b.** Exponential function **c.** Not a function

Look Back

6. How do you know what kind of function the charges are without graphing? ____________

____

SOLVE ANOTHER PROBLEM

The video rental store rents game systems as follows.

Rental Time	Rental Fee
One day or portion thereof	$ 8.00
over 1 day up to 2 days	$12.00
over 2 days up to 4 days	$20.00

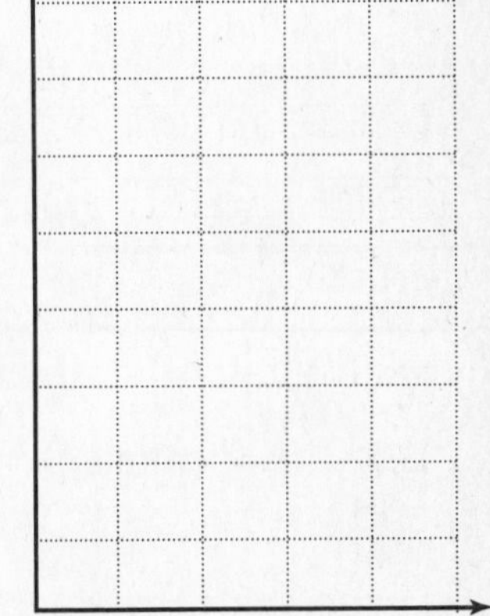

a. Graph the function.

b. What kind of function is this? ____________

Name ______________________________

Guided Problem Solving
10-5

GPS PROBLEM 23, STUDENT PAGE 536

At Epcot Center in Orlando, Florida, the Spaceship Earth is built in the shape of a sphere with a diameter of approximately 165 ft. Use $\pi = 3.14$ to answer each question.

a. Use the formula $S = 4\pi r^2$, where S = surface area and r = radius to find the approximate surface area.

b. Using the formula $V = \frac{4}{3}\pi r^3$, where V = volume and r = radius, find the approximate volume.

Understand

1. What is the diameter? ____________
2. Underline the value of π that you will use.
3. Write the formula for surface area. ____________ For volume. ____________

Plan

4. What is the radius of the sphere? ____________
5. Find the value of r^2. ____________ Of r^3. ____________
6. Complete the equation to find the surface area. $S =$ ____________
7. Complete the equation to find the volume. $V =$ ____________

Solve

8. Solve each equation.

   a. Surface area ____________ **b.** Volume ____________

Look Back

9. Why did you find r^2 and r^3 as the first step in solving both formulas?

____

SOLVE ANOTHER PROBLEM

A museum has an exhibit within a sphere with a diameter of approximately 40 feet. Use $\pi = 3.14$ to answer each question.

a. Use the formula $S = 4\pi r^2$, where S = surface area and r = radius to find the approximate surface area. ____________

b. Using the formula $V = \frac{4}{3}\pi r^3$, where V = volume and r = radius, find the approximate volume. ____________

Name ______________________

Guided Problem Solving
10-6

GPS **PROBLEM 27, STUDENT PAGE 541**

When asked to simplify $x^2 + x^2$, four students got the following answers. Who is correct? What do you think each of the students did to get their answer?

a. Willard's answer is x^4.

b. Bryant's answer is $2x^4$.

c. Katie's answer is $2x^2$.

d. Matt's answer is x^2.

Understand

1. What polynomial are you asked to simplify? ____________

2. What are you asked to find? ______________________

Plan

3. How do you add like terms? ________

a. Add exponents.

b. Add coefficients (numbers multiplying each variable).

Solve

4. Which student has the correct answer? ______________

5. How did Willard find his answer? ______________________

6. How did Bryant find his answer? ______________________

7. How did Katie find her answer? ______________________

8. How did Matt find his answer? ______________________

Look Back

9. Write each term as $1x^2$. Then use the distributive property to find the sum. ______________________

SOLVE ANOTHER PROBLEM

When asked to simplify $4x^3 + x^3$, three students got the following answers. Who is correct? Write how you think each student got their answer.

Correct answer: ____________

a. Su-mi's answer is $4x^6$. ______________________

b. Lizzie's answer is $5x^3$. ______________________

c. Mato's answer is $5x^6$. ______________________

Name ______________________________

Guided Problem Solving
10-7

GPS PROBLEM 25, STUDENT PAGE 547

How much higher does a disc propelled upwards with an initial velocity of 40 m/sec go, over time, than one propelled at 30 m/sec from a platform 8 m high? Subtract $-5t^2 + 30t + 8$ from $-5t^2 + 40t$.

Understand

1. Underline the two polynomials you will use when you subtract.

Plan

2. Order the steps below to show how to subtract polynomials.

_______ Combine like terms

_______ Add the opposite of the second polynomial

_______ Group like terms.

_______ Find the opposite of all terms in the parentheses.

3. Write the polynomials you will subtract as an expression.

_______________ – _______________

Solve

4. Use the steps in Item 2 to subtract the polynomial in Item 3.

a. Step 1: ______________________________

b. Step 2: ______________________________

c. Step 3: ______________________________

d. Step 4: ______________________________

Look Back

5. Show how to write the problem vertically. Then solve to check your answer.

____

____

____

SOLVE ANOTHER PROBLEM

How much higher does a rocket propelled upwards with an initial velocity of 36 m/sec go, over time, than one propelled at 25 m/sec from a platform 10 m high? Subtract $-5t^2 + 25t + 10$ from $-5t^2 + 36t$. _______________

Name ______________________________

Guided Problem Solving
10-8

GPS **PROBLEM 22, STUDENT PAGE 551**

Find an expression for the area of each region and the total area of the figure. Simplify if possible.

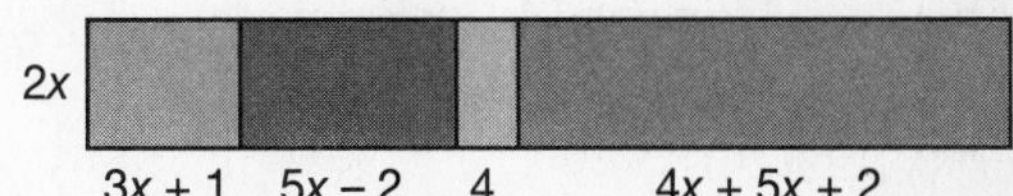

Understand

1. What shape is each region? ______________

2. What is the height of each region? ______

Plan

3. Number the regions from 1 to 4 starting with the region on the left.

4. Add to find the base of the entire figure. ____________

5. What is the formula to find the area of each region? ____________

Solve

6. Use the formula in Item 5 to find each area. Then simplify, if possible.

 a. Region 1 ______________________________

 b. Region 2 ______________________________

 c. Region 3 ______________________________

 d. Region 4 ______________________________

 e. Total area ______________________________

Look Back

7. What is another way to find the total area? ______________________

SOLVE ANOTHER PROBLEM

Find an expression for each region and the total area of the figure. Simplify if possible.

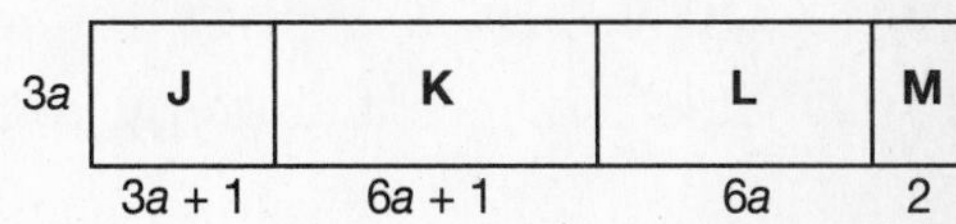

a. Region J ______________________________

b. Region K ______________________________

c. Region L ______________ d. Region M ______________

e. Total area of figure ______________________________

Name ______________________________

Guided Problem Solving
11-1

GPS PROBLEM 4, STUDENT PAGE 567

The two trapezoids are similar.

a. Find *x*.

b. Find the measure of ∠1.

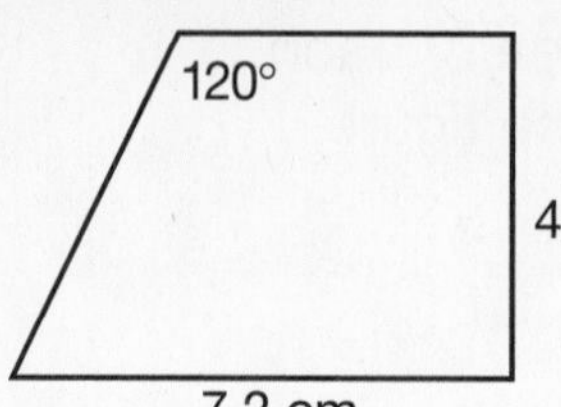

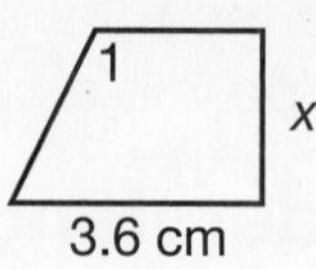

Understand

1. Underline the length that corresponds to *x*.

2. Circle the angle measure that corresponds to ∠1.

3. How are the two figures alike? ______________________________

Plan

4. In similar figures, what is the relationship between

a. corresponding sides? ______________________________

b. corresponding angles? ______________________________

5. Give the measures of two corresponding sides. ______________________________

6. Use the measures in Item 5 to find the similarity ratio. __________

7. Write a proportion using the similarity ratio to find *x*. ______________

Solve

8. Find the length of *x*. __________

9. Find the measure of ∠1. __________

Look Back

10. What is a different strategy you could use to find the answer?

____

SOLVE ANOTHER PROBLEM

The two parallelograms are similar.

a. Find *y*. __________

b. Find the measure of ∠1. __________

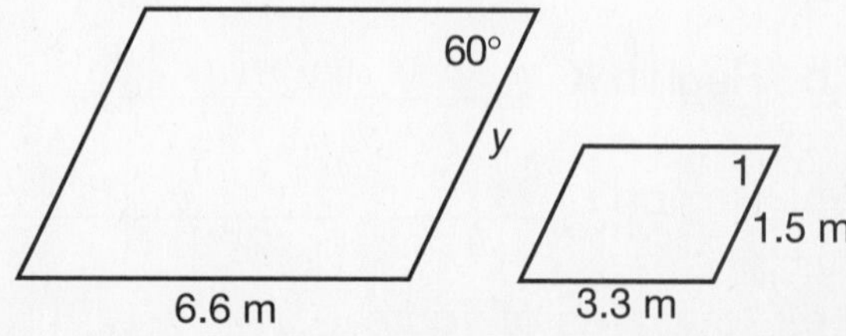

Name ______________________________

Guided Problem Solving
11-2

PROBLEM 7, STUDENT PAGE 572

In the figure, the polygons are congruent. Find the value of x.

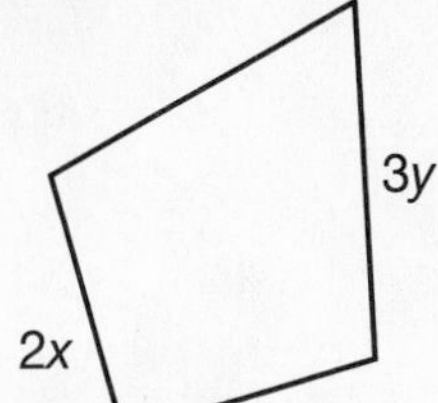

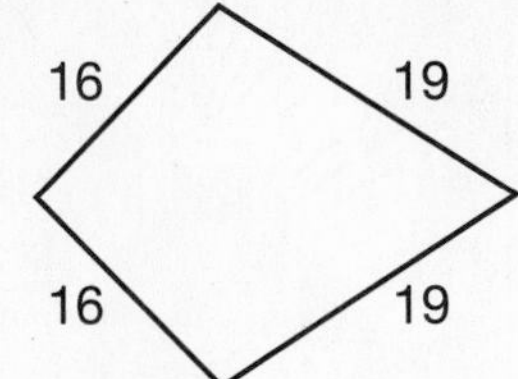

Understand

1. What are the lengths of the sides of the polygon on the right? ______________

2. What are the lengths of the sides of the polygon on the left? ______________

3. What makes two figures congruent? ______________________________

____

Plan

4. What is true about the measures of corresponding sides in congruent figures? ______________

5. What is the measure of the side corresponding to $2x$? ________

6. Write an equation using the lengths of the corresponding sides. ________

7. How will you solve the equation? ______________________________

Solve

8. Find the value of x. __________

Look Back

9. Why don't the figures look the same? ______________________________

____

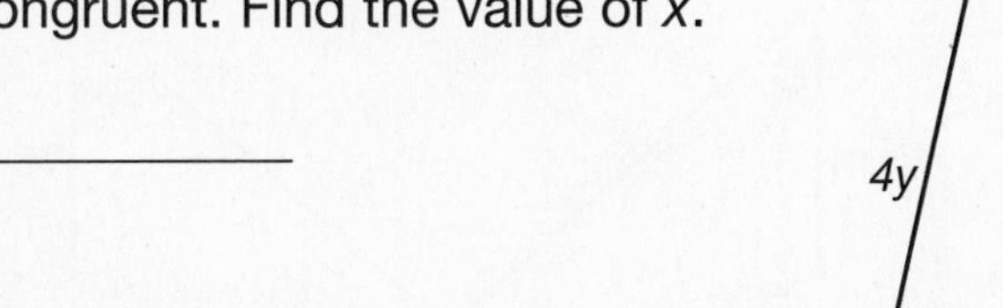

SOLVE ANOTHER PROBLEM

In the figure, the polygons are congruent. Find the value of x.

____

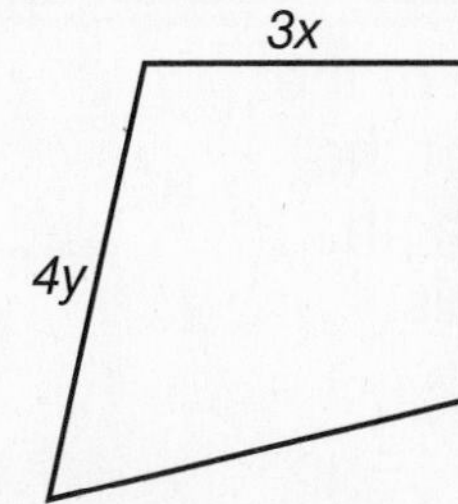

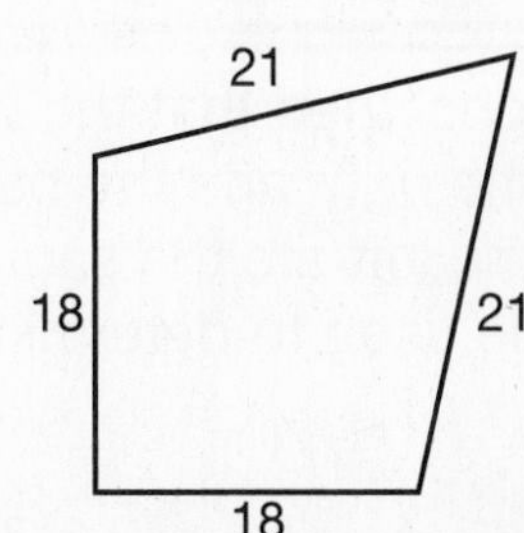

Name ______________________________

Guided Problem Solving
11-3

GPS PROBLEM 11, STUDENT PAGE 578

A surveyor at this native-plant preservation area concludes that the fences on the right and left sides of the land are the same length. State the rule used to determine this.

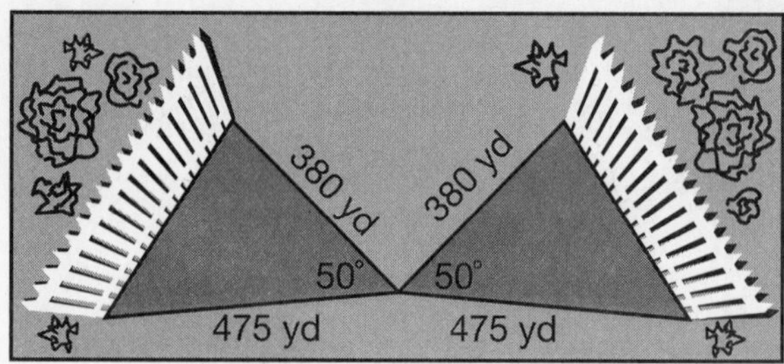

Understand

1. What are the measures of the sides and the angles in each triangle?

	Sides	Angles
a. Triangle on the left	____________	______
b. Triangle on the right	____________	______

2. How can showing that the sides are congruent prove that the fences have equal length? ______________________________

____

Plan

3. Are the angles congruent? Explain. ______________________________

4. Are the given sides congruent? Explain. ______________________________

5. What are the positions of any congruent sides and angles?

____

Solve

6. What rule tells you that the triangles are congruent? __________

Look Back

7. How could the surveyor check his answer? ______________________________

SOLVE ANOTHER PROBLEM

A student concluded that the base of the triangle on the right and the base of the triangle on the left are the same length. State the rule used to determine this.

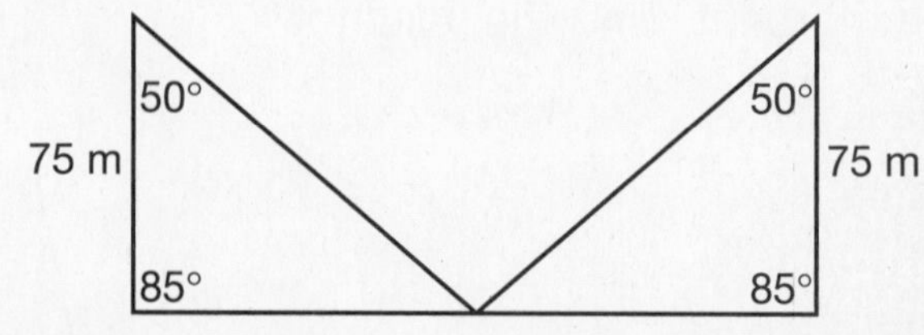

____

Name ________________________________

Guided Problem Solving
11-4

PROBLEM 10, STUDENT PAGE 583

A model rocket travels straight up from its launch pad. At a point, there is a 55° angle. Determine the distance between the nose of the rocket and the launch pad.

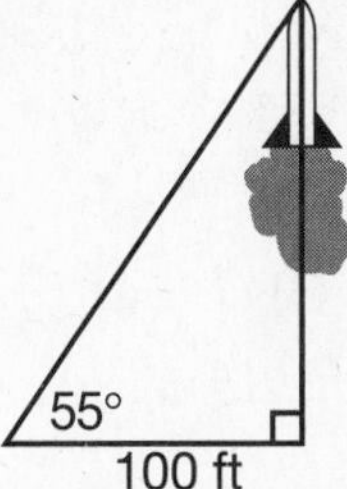

Understand

1. What kind of triangle is formed by the point, the nose of the rocket, and the launch pad? ____________________

2. What is the distance from the launch pad to the point? ________

Plan

3. Is the side showing the distance the rocket travels opposite or adjacent to the 55° angle? ____________

4. Which ratio will you use to find the distance traveled? ______

   a. $\sin 55° = \frac{\text{opposite}}{\text{hypotenuse}}$ **b.** $\cos 55° = \frac{\text{adjacent}}{\text{hypotenuse}}$ **c.** $\tan 55° = \frac{\text{opposite}}{\text{adjacent}}$

5. Use your calculator or a table to find the decimal value to the nearest thousandth of the ratio you chose in Item 4. ________

Solve

6. Substitute known values in the equation you chose in Item 4. ______________

7. Solve your equation. What is the distance between the nose of the rocket and the launch pad? ________

Look Back

8. How could you use another ratio to find the distance between the nose of the rocket and the launch pad? ____________________

____

____

SOLVE ANOTHER PROBLEM

A model rocket travels straight up from its launch pad. At a point, there is a 50° angle. Determine the distance between the nose of the rocket and the launch pad.

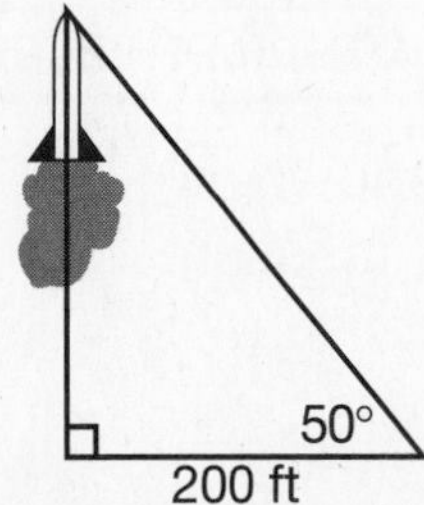

____

Name ______________________________

Guided Problem Solving
11-5

GPS PROBLEM 5, STUDENT PAGE 588

On the two triangles shown, $\triangle CBD \sim \triangle CAE$. If $\overline{CD}$ measures 5 cm, what does $\overline{CE}$ measure?

(A) 7.6 cm (B) 7.3 cm

(C) 7.1 cm (D) 7.9 cm

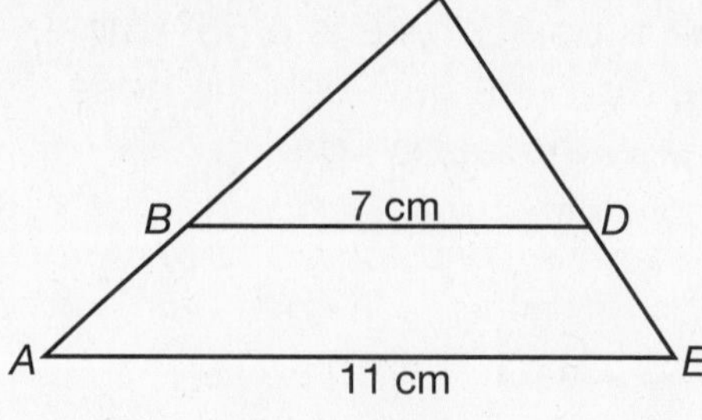

Understand

1. What does the symbol ~ mean? ______________

2. What is the length of *CD*? ________

3. What are you asked to find? ______________

Plan

4. Identify the corresponding side to each side below.

a. $\overline{AE}$ ________ **b.** $\overline{CE}$ ________

5. Write a ratio for the corresponding sides. ________

6. Set up a proportion using the given values for the lengths of the sides. Let *x* represent the unknown side. ____________

Solve

7. Solve the proportion. ____________

8. Which answer choice is the correct one? ____________

Look Back

9. Why aren't the correct answer choice and your answer to Item 7 the same?

____

SOLVE ANOTHER PROBLEM

On the two triangles shown, $\triangle ABC \sim \triangle ADE$. If *AC* measures 4 m, what does *AE* measure?

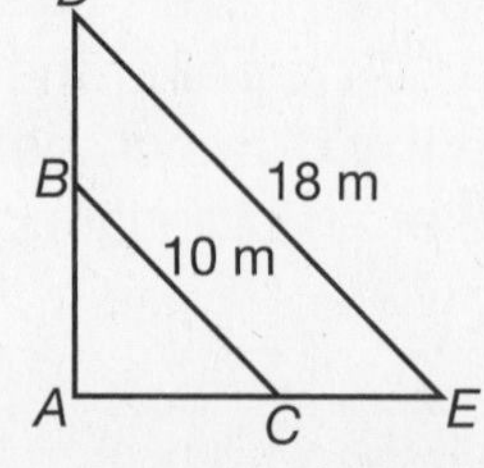

____

Name ______________________________

Guided Problem Solving 11-6

GPS PROBLEM 9, STUDENT PAGE 599

What transformation, if any, will turn this shape into a math word you've recently learned? (Turning the page and using a mirror may help you decide.)

ROTATE

Understand

1. What will the collection of shapes make when transformed? ______________
2. Is it possible that the shapes cannot be transformed? _______
3. Is it possible that more than one transformation can show the same result? _______

Plan

4. If you translate the shape, will a slide help you read the word? _______
5. If you reflect the shape by using a mirror, can you read the word? _______
6. If you rotate the shape 180°, can you read the word? _______

Solve

7. What word do the shapes make when transformed? ______________
8. What is the transformation(s)? ______________

Look Back

9. How could sketching a coordinate grid around the shapes help you find the word? ______________________________

____

____

SOLVE ANOTHER PROBLEM

What transformation, if any, will turn this shape into a math word you've recently learned? (Turning the page and using a mirror may help you decide.)

CONGRUENT

____

Name ________________________________

Guided Problem Solving
11-7

Reflect the figure across the *y*-axis and give the new coordinates.

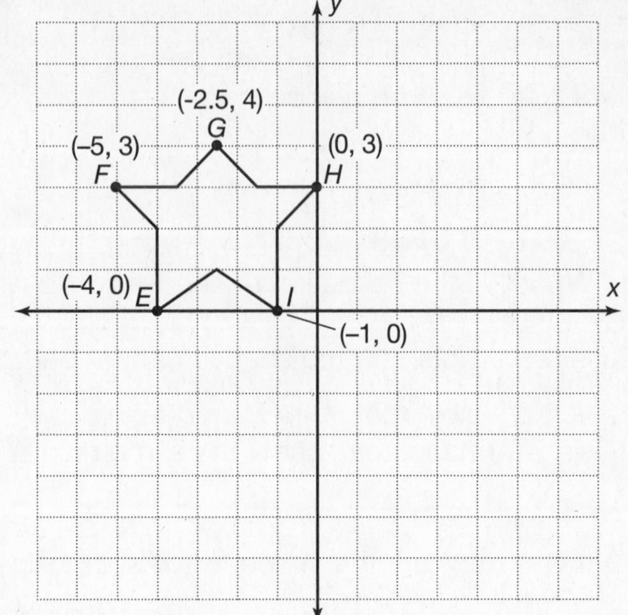

Understand

1. What shape is the figure?

____

2. Across which axis will you reflect the figure?

____

3. What else are you asked for?

____

Plan

4. Name the coordinates of the figure above.

E ________ *F* ________ *G* ________ *H* ________ *I* ________

5. Will the distance from the *y*-axis change or stay the same? ________________

6. How will the coordinates change when reflected across the *y*-axis? ________________

____

Solve

7. Graph the reflection. What are the new coordinates?

E′ ________ *F′* ________ *G′* ________ *H′* ________ *I′* ________

Look Back

8. Why does one point not change when the figure is reflected?

____

SOLVE ANOTHER PROBLEM

Reflect the figure in the grid above across the *x*-axis and give the new coordinates.

E″ ________ *F″* ________ *G″* ________ *H″* ________ *I″* ________

Name ______________________________

Guided Problem Solving
11-8

GPS PROBLEM 4, STUDENT PAGE 608

How many degrees does it take for a regular octagon to rotate onto itself?

Understand

1. What is a regular octagon? ______________________________

2. Why will you ignore the word STOP in the center of the sign?

____

Plan

3. How can you tell if the octagon rotates onto itself? ______________________________

4. How many times can an octagon rotate on itself? Count the final turn to return to the original position. __________

5. How many degrees are in a complete rotation? ________

6. How can you find the number of degrees in each turn? ______________________________

Solve

7. List the degrees of the rotations.

____

Look Back

8. How can you check your answer? ______________________________

SOLVE ANOTHER PROBLEM

How many degrees does it take for a regular hexagon to rotate onto itself?

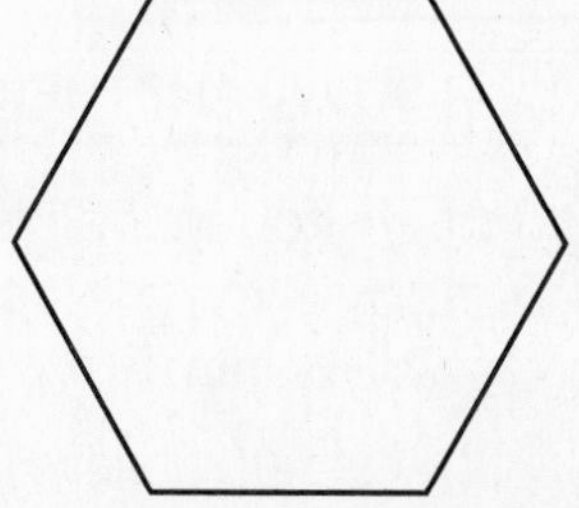

____

Name ______________________________

Guided Problem Solving 11-9

GPS PROBLEM 11, STUDENT PAGE 614

A flooring contractor has 175 tiles that are 6 in. by 6 in. for covering a kitchen floor that is 15 ft by 10 ft. Does he have enough tiles? Explain.

Understand

1. How many tiles does the contractor have? ____________

2. What are the dimensions of each tile? ________________

3. What are the dimensions of the floor? ________________

Plan

4. Use decimals to write the dimensions of the tiles in feet. ________________

5. What is the area of each tile in square feet? ____________

6. What is the area of the kitchen floor? ____________

7. How can you find the number of tiles needed to cover the floor? ____________________________________

Solve

8. How many tiles are needed to cover the floor? ____________

9. Does he have enough tiles? Explain. ________________________________

____

Look Back

10. How could you find the answer in another way? __________________________

____

SOLVE ANOTHER PROBLEM

A section of a kitchen wall is 4 ft by 7 ft. It will be covered with tiles that are 3 in. by 3 in. The contractor has 450 tiles. Does she have enough tiles? Explain.

____

Name ______________________________

Guided Problem Solving
12-1

GPS PROBLEM 11, STUDENT PAGE 630

One word is to be chosen from each list. How many sentences can be made?

article	adjective	noun	verb	adverb
The	quick	dog	ran	quickly
A	smelly	robot	slipped	badly
	purple	king	cooked	
	scraggly		scratched	
			waited	

Understand

1. How many words are in each list?

   a. Article __________ b. Adjective __________ c. Noun __________

   d. Verb __________ e. Adverb __________

2. How many words will be chosen from each list? __________

3. Do you need to be concerned with how well the sentences read? ________

Plan

4. How can you use the Counting Principle to find the number of sentences?

   ____

5. Write an expression to find the number of sentences. __________

Solve

6. Simplify your expression in Item 5.
   How many sentences can be made. __________

Look Back

7. What is a different way to find the answer? Which way is easier? Explain. __________

   ____

SOLVE ANOTHER PROBLEM

School shirts can be ordered through the Student Council. How many different shirts are possible?

color	sleeve	size	style	design
blue	short	small	tee	name only
gold	long	medium	sweat	name and logo
		large	jersey	
		x-large		

____

Name ____________________

Guided Problem Solving
12-2

GPS PROBLEM 22, STUDENT PAGE 636

Mr. Lehr has 8 groups in his math class. Tomorrow, 3 of the groups will give their group-project reports. How many different ways can he select and order the groups?

Understand

1. How many groups are in the class? ____________

2. How many groups will give reports tomorrow? ____________

3. What are you asked to find? ____________

____

Plan

4. How many groups will *not* give reports tomorrow? ____________

5. Use factorial notation to write the number of ways to order

   a. all the groups. ________ b. the groups not selected. ________

6. Use factorial notation to write an expression to show how many different ways Mr. Lehr can select and order the groups. ________

Solve

7. How many different ways can Mr. Lehr select and order the groups? ____________

8. Write a sentence to give the final answer. ____________

____

Look Back

9. Rewrite the expression in Item 6 using factors instead of factorial notation.

____

SOLVE ANOTHER PROBLEM

Mrs. Lenzi has 7 groups in her math class. Next Monday, 4 of the groups will give their group-project reports. How many different ways can she select and order the groups? ____________

Name ______________________

Guided Problem Solving
12-3

PROBLEM 11, STUDENT PAGE 641

How many ways could you select 3 possible components for a sound system from a tape-deck, CD player, laser disk, equalizer, and surround-sound stereo?

Understand

1. Circle the number of components that will be in the sound system.
2. Underline the possible components to include in the system.
3. Are you asked for how the system can be assembled or the number of ways it can be assembled? ______________

Plan

4. Write each in factorial notation.

   a. number of ways to select and arrange all components ________

   b. number of ways to arrange the selected components ________

   c. number of ways to arrange the components that are *not* selected ________

5. Which shows the number of ways to assemble the sound system? ________

   a. $\frac{5!}{3!}$ b. $\frac{5!}{3! \times 2!}$

   c. $\frac{3! \times 2!}{5!}$ d. $\frac{3!}{2!}$

Solve

6. How many ways could you select 3 components for the sound-system? ______________

Look Back

7. Check your answer by making a list of the possible sound-system components. Use *T*, *C*, *L*, *E*, and *S* to represent the components.

____

____

SOLVE ANOTHER PROBLEM

How many ways could you make a hamburger with 4 toppings if the available toppings are tomato, cheese, onion, pickle, lettuce, bacon, and relish? ______________

Name ______________________________

Guided Problem Solving
12-4

GPS PROBLEM 14, STUDENT PAGE 650

The yellow and green sectors of the spinner are each $\frac{1}{4}$ of the spinner area.

What is the probability of not spinning green?

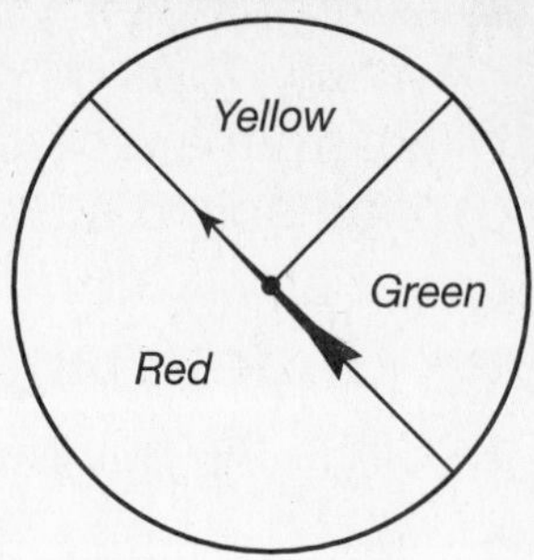

Understand

1. How many sections are shown on the spinner? __________

2. Which sectors have the same area? ______________________

3. What fraction of the area is red? ______

Plan

4. How can you make the red sector have the same area as the green sector? __________________

5. How can you find the probability of an event? ______

   a. $P = \frac{\text{number of outcomes in the event}}{\text{number of outcomes in sample space}}$

   b. $P = \frac{\text{number of events}}{\text{number of events in sample space}}$

6. List the equally-likely outcomes. Some colors may be listed more than one time. ______________________

7. List the outcomes that are *not* green. ______________________

Solve

8. Write the probability of not spinning green as a fraction. ______

Look Back

9. How can you use subtraction to find the answer? ______________________

____

SOLVE ANOTHER PROBLEM

The white and black sectors of the spinner are each $\frac{1}{5}$ of the spinner area. What is the probability of not spinning black?

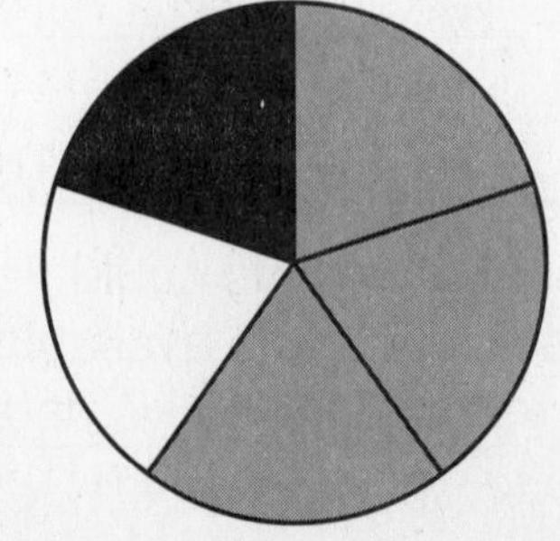

______

Name ______________________________

Guided Problem Solving
12-5

GPS PROBLEM 11, STUDENT PAGE 656

Cliff surveyed his class to find the day of the month each person was born and organized his data in a stem and leaf diagram.

a. What is the probability that a student was born on the 17th?

b. What is the probability that a student was born after the 29th?

c. What is the probability that a student was not born on the 4th?

Stem	Leaf
0	1 3 5 7 7 8 8 9
1	1 1 3 5 6 7 7 7 8 9
2	0 0 1 2 2 3 4 6 6 7 8 9
3	0 0 1

Understand

1. What does each response represent? ______________________________

Plan

2. How many outcomes are in the sample space? ____________________

3. Write the number of students that were born each date.

a. 17th ____________ **b.** 30th or 31st ____________ **c.** 4th ____________

4. How many students were *not* born on the 4th? ____________________

Solve

5. Write the probability that a student was born on each given date.

a. 17th ____________ **b.** after the 29th ____________ **c.** not on 4th ____________

Look Back

6. Write each probability in Item 5 as a percent.

a. 17th ________ **b.** after the 29th ________ **c.** not on 4th ________

SOLVE ANOTHER PROBLEM

Add two more birthdates, the ninth and the twenty-ninth to Cliff's stem and leaf diagram above. Then answer the questions below.

a. What is the probability that a student was born on the 25th? ________

b. What is the probability that a student was born after the 16th? ________

c. What is the probability that a student was not born on the 10th? ________

Name ______________________________

Guided Problem Solving
12-6

PROBLEM 7, STUDENT PAGE 661

You roll a pair of number cubes in a board game. If the first cube comes up a 6, find the probability that the sum of the two number cubes is:

a. 6 **b.** 7 **c.** greater than 10 **d.** greater than 6

Understand

1. How many number cubes will you roll? ____________
2. Circle the number that came up when the first cube was rolled.

Plan

3. What are the possible outcomes for the second number cube? ____________
4. List the possible outcomes for the two rolls.

a. 6 + ____ = ____ **b.** 6 + ____ = ____ **c.** 6 + ____ = ____

d. 6 + ____ = ____ **e.** 6 + ____ = ____ **f.** 6 + ____ = ____

5. Which sums are greater than 10? ________ Greater than 6? ________

Solve

6. Use the data in Item 4 to find each probability.

a. P(sum is 6) = ______ **b.** P(sum is 7) = ______

c. P(sum > 10) = ______ **d.** P(sum is > 6) = ______

Look Back

7. Which probability can you determine without listing the possible outcomes in Item 4? Explain. ____________

____

____

SOLVE ANOTHER PROBLEM

You roll a pair of number cubes in a board game. If the first cube comes up a 4, find the probability that the sum of the two number cubes is:

a. 6 **b.** 11 **c.** less than 8 **d.** greater than 5

____ ____ ____ ____

Name ____________________

Guided Problem Solving
12-7

PROBLEM 17, STUDENT PAGE 667

You enter a contest on your birthday. Suppose you win a prize in the contest.

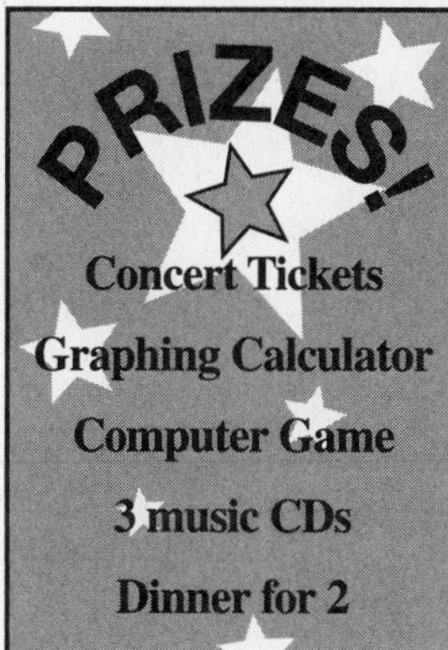

a. If the prizes are chosen at random, what is your chance of winning the concert tickets?

b. If the first place winner chose the graphing calculator, what are your chances of winning the concert tickets now?

Understand

1. How many different prizes are possible? ____________
2. How are the prizes awarded? ____________
3. Is the prize awarded to subsequent winners dependent or independent of the prizes awarded to prior winners? ____________

Plan

4. How many outcomes (prizes) are available to the first winner? ____________
5. How many outcomes are available to the second winner? ____________
6. How many outcomes (prizes) can you win? ____________

Solve

7. What is your chance of getting the concert tickets if you are the first winner? ____________
8. If you are the second winner, what are your chances of winning concert tickets if the calculator has already been awarded? ____________

Look Back

9. As other prizes are awarded to other winners, are you more or less likely to win the concert tickets? Explain.

____

SOLVE ANOTHER PROBLEM

Prizes at a raffle are $100, $75, $25, $25, $25, and $25.

a. If the prizes are chosen at random, what is your chance of winning $75? ____________

b. If the $100 prize has already been won, what are your chances of winning $75? ____________

Name ______________________________

Guided Problem Solving 1-1

PROBLEM 8, STUDENT PAGE 10

When the city schools take a two-week winter holiday, a skating rink gives students under 18 a discount to skate on weekdays. Make a stem-and-leaf diagram using a table which shows the daily number of students that take advantage of this discount. What days are represented in the stem with the most leaves?

Mon.	Tue.	Wed.	Thur.	Fri.	Mon.	Tue.	Wed.	Thur.	Fri.
64	52	57	51	42	44	39	42	52	55

Understand

1. Circle the way you are asked to display the data.
2. Underline what you are asked to find.

Plan

3. List the data in order from least to greatest.
   39, 42, 42, 44, 51, 52, 52, 55, 57, 64.
4. What is the range of data? 39 to 64, or 25.

Solve

5. Arrange the stems in numerical order.
6. List the ones digits of each stem in increasing order.
7. Which stem has the most leaves? 5
8. Name the days represented in the stem with the most leaves.
   Tue., Wed., Thur., Fri.

Stem	Leaf
3	9
4	2 2 4
5	1 2 2 5 7
6	4

Look Back

9. How can you be sure you have recorded all the data? Possible answer:
   The number of leaves equals the number of days.

SOLVE ANOTHER PROBLEM

Make a stem-and-leaf diagram of the quiz scores below. Which quizzes are represented in the stem with the most leaves? Quizzes 5, 8, 9, 10.

Quiz	1	2	3	4	5	6	7	8	9	10
Score	95	75	63	77	89	99	75	84	81	81

Stem	Leaf
6	3
7	5 5 7
8	1 1 4 9
9	5 9

Name ______________________________

Guided Problem Solving 1-2

PROBLEM 5, STUDENT PAGE 15

Find the mean, median, and mode for the data set.

During 1982–1990, the annual number of oil tanker spills worldwide was 9, 17, 15, 9, 8, 12, 13, 31, and 8. Identify the outlier and calculate the mean and median as if the outlier were not in the data set.

Understand

1. Circle the data set.
2. What is an outlier? An extreme value.

Plan

3. List the data in order from least to greatest.
   8, 8, 9, 9, 12, 13, 15, 17, 31
4. How many data values are in the data set? 9 values.

Solve

5. For the data set of oil tanker spills from 1982–1990, find the
   a. mean. $13.\overline{5}$ b. median. 12 c. mode. 8 and 9
6. What is the outlier? 31
7. What is the mean without the outlier as part of the data? 11.375
8. What is the median without the outlier as part of the data? 10.5

Look Back

9. How did the mean and median change when you calculated them without the outlier? Why? Possible answer:
   Decreased because the greatest value was removed.

SOLVE ANOTHER PROBLEM

Find the mean, median, and mode of the data set naming the number of minutes some students spent on chores last night: 18, 24, 47, 31, 21, 29. Identify the outlier and calculate the mean and median as if the outlier were not in the data set. Mean $28.\overline{3}$, Median 26.5;
Mode-None; Outlier: 47; Rev. mean: 24.6, median: 24.

Name ______________________________

Guided Problem Solving 1-3

PROBLEM 2, STUDENT PAGE 20

Sketch a box-and-whisker plot for the set of data. Between what values does the middle half of the data fall?

During the 1980s, the largest major earthquakes around the world registered 7.3, 7.2, 7.7, 7.1, 7.8, 8.1, 7.3, 6.5, 7.3, 6.8, and 6.9 on the Richter Scale.

Understand

Possible answer: Item 7

1. Circle the information you need to sketch a box-and-whiskers plot.

Plan

2. Arrange the data in order from least to greatest.
   6.5, 6.8, 6.9, 7.1, 7.2, 7.3, 7.3, 7.3, 7.7, 7.8, 8.1
3. What is the range? 6.5 to 8.1 or 1.6 The median? 7.3
4. What is the median of the lower half? 6.9 Of the upper half? 7.7

Solve

5. Draw the box-and-whisker plot using the range, the median, and the lower and the upper quartiles for the data. Write a title.

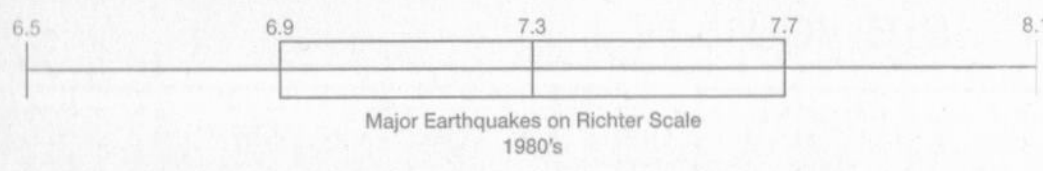

6. Between what values does the middle half fall? 6.9 and 7.7

Look Back

7. What other ways could you display the data? Stem-and-leaf diagram.

SOLVE ANOTHER PROBLEM

Sketch a box-and-whisker plot for the set of data showing the days spent on lab projects: 34, 32, 50, 16, 29, 37, 44, 29, 18, 22, 40 and 32. Between what values does the middle half of the data fall? 25.5 and 38.5

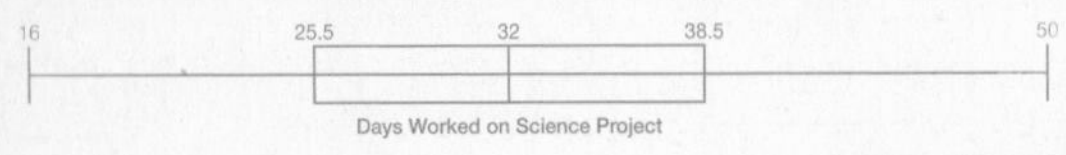

Name ______________________________

Guided Problem Solving 1-4

PROBLEM 4, STUDENT PAGE 26

Draw a line graph of the average monthly production of cars (in thousands) from 1986 to 1992. About how many cars were made in 1990?

Year	1986	1987	1988	1989	1990	1991	1992
Cars	474	451	504	567	592	590	626

Possible answers: 3, 5, 7, 9

Understand

1. What kind of graph do you need to draw? Line graph.

Plan

2. Which operation will you use to find yearly production? Multiplication.
3. How will you scale the vertical axis? Why might you have a break in the scale? 0, 450–650, intervals of 25;
   Because of the large break in the data.
4. How will you scale the horizontal axis?
   1986 to 1992.

Solve

5. Scale the axes.
6. Plot the number of cars produced each year and draw a line through each point, connecting them.
7. Label each axis and title the graph.
8. About how many cars were made in 1990?
   About 7,104,000 cars.

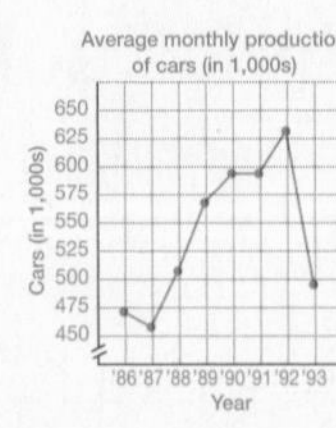

Look Back

9. Would the graph be easier to read with or without a break in the scale? Explain. With a break, since data is closer to horizontal axis' labels.

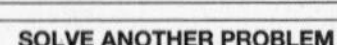

SOLVE ANOTHER PROBLEM

There were 5,961,000 cars produced in 1993. Find the average monthly production and add this data to your line graph above. ≈ 497,000.

Name ______________________________

Guided Problem Solving 1-5

GPS PROBLEM 5, STUDENT PAGE 35

State the population and whether or not the sample is random.

For the population of country music fans: randomly chosen attendees of a country music concert are asked about their favorite performers.

Understand

1. What two things are you asked to find? Population and whether or not the sample is random.
2. Who makes up the sample? Country music concert attendees.

Plan

3. How were the attendees chosen? At random.
4. Are the people attending the concert biased? Explain. Yes. They are probably biased for the performers at this concert.

Solve

5. What is the population? Country music fans.
6. Is the sample representative of all country music fans? Explain. No; those fans who couldn't attend the concert are excluded.

Look Back

7. Is the sample size representative of the population? No, it is too small, since concert attendees are only a minute segment of the millions of country music fans.

SOLVE ANOTHER PROBLEM

State the population and whether or not the sample is random.

The Pep Club sold 800 raffle tickets. One stub from each ticket was placed in a bin. The bin was shaken and 5 tickets were drawn for prizes.

Population: raffle ticket buyers; It is random.

Name ______________________________

Guided Problem Solving 1-6

GPS PROBLEM 2, STUDENT PAGE 40

Asteroids are chunks of rock orbiting the sun. Most of them are between the orbits of Mars and Jupiter. Astronomers have studied 105 of them to see how fast they rotate. The data is rounded to the nearest rotation and summarized in this histogram.

a. How many asteroids have rotation speeds of four per day?

b. Make a frequency table for this histogram.

c. What is the mode?

The Speed of Asteroids

Understand

1. Circle what you are asked to make.

Plan

2. Label the columns in the frequency table.

Solve

3. How many asteroids have rotation speeds of four? 15 asteroids.
4. Complete the frequency table.
5. What is the mode? 5 rotations.

Rotations	Number of Asteroids
1	6
2	10
3	9
4	15
5	23
6	10
7	7
8	10
9	7
10	5
11	3

Look Back

6. How do you know that all data is recorded? Sum of frequencies = 105.

SOLVE ANOTHER PROBLEM

Absences in each of Mrs. Reynolds classes are summarized in this graph.

a. How many have 5 absences? 2 classes.

b. Make a frequency table of this data on another sheet of paper. Check students' answers.

c. What is the mode? 0 absences.

Absences in Mrs. Reynold's class

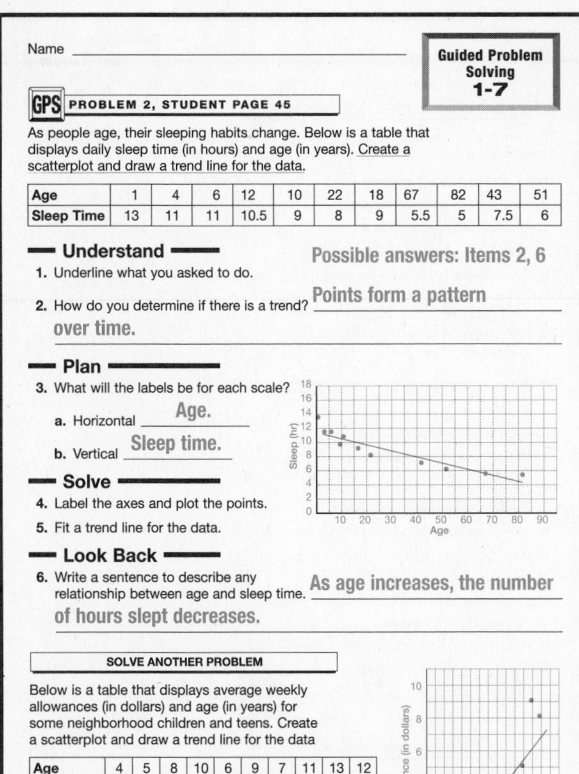

Name ______________________________

Guided Problem Solving 1-7

GPS PROBLEM 2, STUDENT PAGE 45

As people age, their sleeping habits change. Below is a table that displays daily sleep time (in hours) and age (in years). Create a scatterplot and draw a trend line for the data.

Age	1	4	6	12	10	22	18	67	82	43	51
Sleep Time	13	11	11	10.5	9	8	9	5.5	5	7.5	6

Understand

Possible answers: Items 2, 6

1. Underline what you asked to do.
2. How do you determine if there is a trend? Points form a pattern over time.

Plan

3. What will the labels be for each scale?

a. Horizontal Age.

b. Vertical Sleep time.

Solve

4. Label the axes and plot the points.
5. Fit a trend line for the data.

Look Back

6. Write a sentence to describe any relationship between age and sleep time. As age increases, the number of hours slept decreases.

SOLVE ANOTHER PROBLEM

Below is a table that displays average weekly allowances (in dollars) and age (in years) for some neighborhood children and teens. Create a scatterplot and draw a trend line for the data

Age	4	5	8	10	6	9	7	11	13	12
Allowance	1	1	3	4	2	4	2	5	8	9

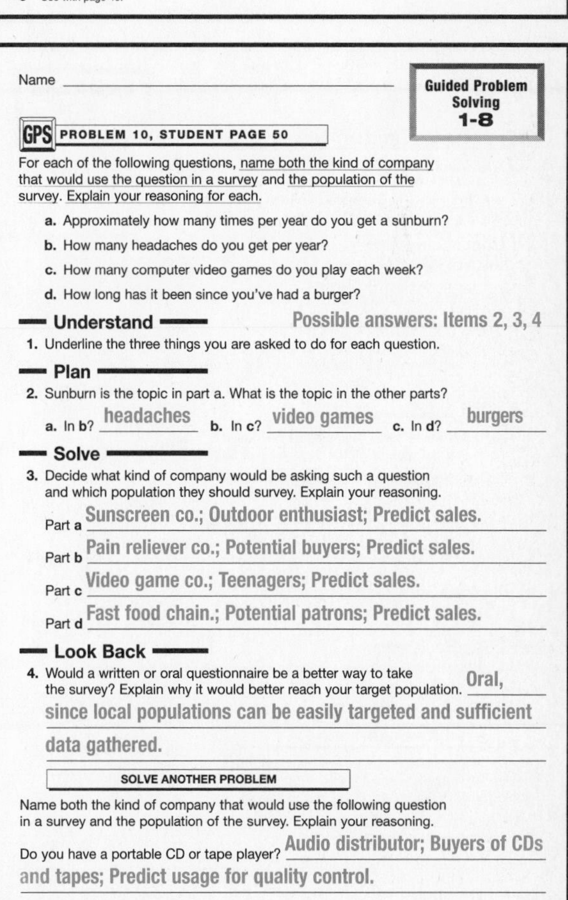

Name ______________________________

Guided Problem Solving 1-8

GPS PROBLEM 10, STUDENT PAGE 50

For each of the following questions, name both the kind of company that would use the question in a survey and the population of the survey. Explain your reasoning for each.

a. Approximately how many times per year do you get a sunburn?

b. How many headaches do you get per year?

c. How many computer video games do you play each week?

d. How long has it been since you've had a burger?

Understand

Possible answers: Items 2, 3, 4

1. Underline the three things you are asked to do for each question.

Plan

2. Sunburn is the topic in part a. What is the topic in the other parts?

a. In b? headaches b. In c? video games c. In d? burgers

Solve

3. Decide what kind of company would be asking such a question and which population they should survey. Explain your reasoning.

Part a Sunscreen co.; Outdoor enthusiast; Predict sales.

Part b Pain reliever co.; Potential buyers; Predict sales.

Part c Video game co.; Teenagers; Predict sales.

Part d Fast food chain.; Potential patrons; Predict sales.

Look Back

4. Would a written or oral questionnaire be a better way to take the survey? Explain why it would better reach your target population. Oral, since local populations can be easily targeted and sufficient data gathered.

SOLVE ANOTHER PROBLEM

Name both the kind of company that would use the following question in a survey and the population of the survey. Explain your reasoning.

Do you have a portable CD or tape player? Audio distributor; Buyers of CDs and tapes; Predict usage for quality control.

Name ______

Guided Problem Solving 2-1

GPS PROBLEM 12, STUDENT PAGE 65

What integer is described by the following? The absolute value is 5 and the number is to the left of 0 on a number line.

Understand

1. Circle the information you need.
2. Underline what you are asked to find.
3. What is an integer?
   Integers are whole numbers and their opposites.
4. What is absolute value?
   The absolute value of a number is the distance it is from zero.
5. Which numbers are to the left of 0? Negative numbers.

Plan

6. What points have an absolute value of 5? 5, –5
7. Draw a number line. Label 0 and the points with absolute values of 5.

–5 0 5

Solve

8. Two points have an absolute value of 5. Which point is to the left of 0 on the number line? –5
9. Answer the question using a complete sentence.
   –5 is the integer whose absolute value is 5 and is to the left of 0 on the number line.

Look Back

10. Could you have found the integer without drawing a number line? How?
    Yes, by mentally counting back 5 spaces from 0.

SOLVE ANOTHER PROBLEM

Find the integer that has an absolute value of 3 and is to the right of 0 on the number line. 3

Name ______

Guided Problem Solving 2-2

GPS PROBLEM 25, STUDENT PAGE 71

An elevator on the 10th floor goes down 9 floors. Then it goes up 19 floors, down 3, and finally up 12. What floor does it end up on? Explain how you arrived at your answer.

Understand

1. Circle the information you need.
2. Underline what you are asked to find.

Plan

3. Think of the movement of the elevator as addition. Going down is shown as negative integers. Which would show the elevator going up?
   Positive integers.
4. Which will help you find the answer? c
   a. 10 + 9 + 19 + 3 + 12
   b. 10 + (–9) + (–19) + (–3) + (–12)
   c. 10 + (–9) + 19 + (–3) + 12

Solve

5. Add to find the floor the elevator ends up on. Use the commutative and associative properties to group integers that have the same sign.
   (10 + 19 + 12) + (–9 + –3) = 29
6. Write a sentence answering the question in the problem. Then explain how you found your answer.
   The elevator ends up on the 29th floor.

Look Back

7. How could you have found the answer using a different method?
   Use the strategy, "Draw a Picture."

SOLVE ANOTHER PROBLEM

At dawn, the temperature was 6°C above freezing. The temperature had risen 10 degrees by noon, and another 5 degrees by 3:00 P.M. before falling 12 degrees. The next morning the temperature had fallen another 6 degrees. What was the temperature the next morning?

3°C

Name ______

Guided Problem Solving 2-3

GPS PROBLEM 17, STUDENT PAGE 75

Last week, Maria saw a dress priced at $53. The sign in the window said there was $5 off any purchase in the store. She decided to wait for a sale. This week, the dress was priced at $49 but there was no discount. She bought the dress. Should she have waited? Explain.

Understand

1. Circle the information you need.
2. Write *$5 off* as an integer. –5

Plan

3. Which expression will help you find the how much Maria would have paid for the dress with the $5 discount? a
   a. 53 + (–5) b. 49 + 5 c. 53 + 5 d. 49 + (–5)

Solve

4. How much would Maria have paid for the dress last week if she took $5 off the dress price of $53? $48
5. Is the amount Maria paid this week more or less than the amount she would have paid last week? More
6. Should Maria have waited to buy the dress? Explain.
   No. It costs $1 more this week than the week before.

Look Back

7. What other number sentences could you have used to find the answer?
   53 – 49 = 4, 4 < 5

SOLVE ANOTHER PROBLEM

Cheryl saw a jacket during a pre-season sale for $15 off the regular price of $47. Today she saw the jacket priced at $35 and she bought it. Should she have bought the jacket during the pre-season sale? Explain.

Yes. The jacket would have cost $3 less.

Name ______

Guided Problem Solving 2-4

GPS PROBLEM 37, STUDENT PAGE 81

The temperature has been falling an average of 4° per hour. If the temperature at 12:00 A.M. is 10°F, what do you predict it will be at 6:00 A.M.?

Understand

1. Circle the information you need.
2. Underline the question.

Plan

3. Find the number of hours from 12:00 A.M. until 6:00 A.M. 6 hours
4. Write an integer for a *falling* temperature of 4°F. –4
5. Will the temperature at 6:00 A.M. be higher or lower than the 12:00 A.M. temperature? Lower
6. Which of the following is a reasonable answer? b
   a. about 0°F b. below 0°F c. above 10°F

Solve

7. Predict how much the temperature will change between 12:00 A.M. and 6:00 A.M. The temperature will drop 24°.
8. Predict the temperature at 6:00 A.M. –14°F
9. Write a sentence predicting the temperature.
   The temperature will be about –14°F at 6:00 A.M.

Look Back

10. How could you have found the answer using a different method?
    Use repeated subtraction.

SOLVE ANOTHER PROBLEM

A water tank has been draining an average of 2 feet per hour. If the level at 8:00 A.M. is 18 feet, at what level do you think the water will be at 4:00 P.M.?

2 feet

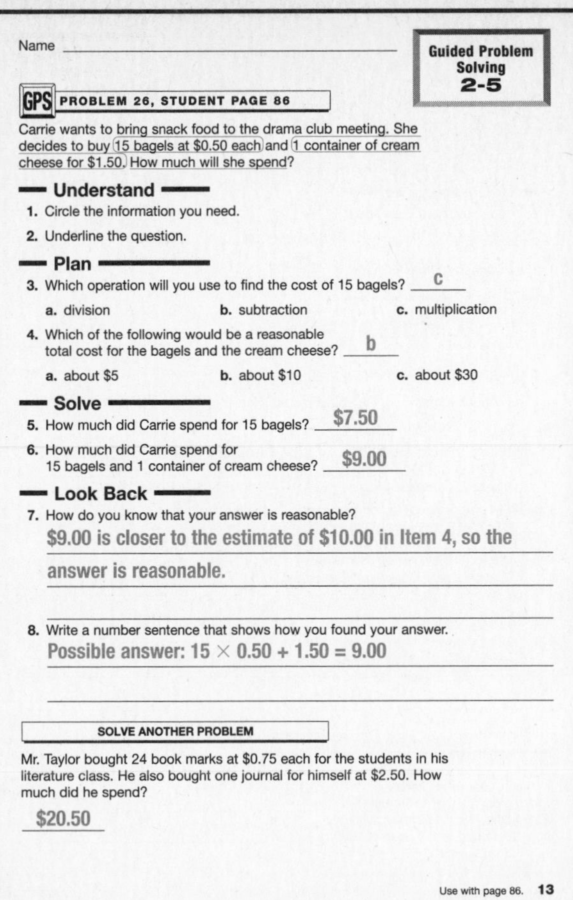

Name ______________________

Guided Problem Solving 2-5

GPS PROBLEM 26, STUDENT PAGE 86

Carrie wants to bring snack food to the drama club meeting. She decides to buy 15 bagels at $0.50 each and 1 container of cream cheese for $1.50. How much will she spend?

Understand

1. Circle the information you need.
2. Underline the question.

Plan

3. Which operation will you use to find the cost of 15 bagels? c

 a. division b. subtraction c. multiplication

4. Which of the following would be a reasonable total cost for the bagels and the cream cheese? b

 a. about $5 b. about $10 c. about $30

Solve

5. How much did Carrie spend for 15 bagels? $7.50
6. How much did Carrie spend for 15 bagels and 1 container of cream cheese? $9.00

Look Back

7. How do you know that your answer is reasonable?
 $9.00 is closer to the estimate of $10.00 in Item 4, so the answer is reasonable.
8. Write a number sentence that shows how you found your answer.
 Possible answer: $15 \times 0.50 + 1.50 = 9.00$

SOLVE ANOTHER PROBLEM

Mr. Taylor bought 24 book marks at $0.75 each for the students in his literature class. He also bought one journal for himself at $2.50. How much did he spend?

$20.50

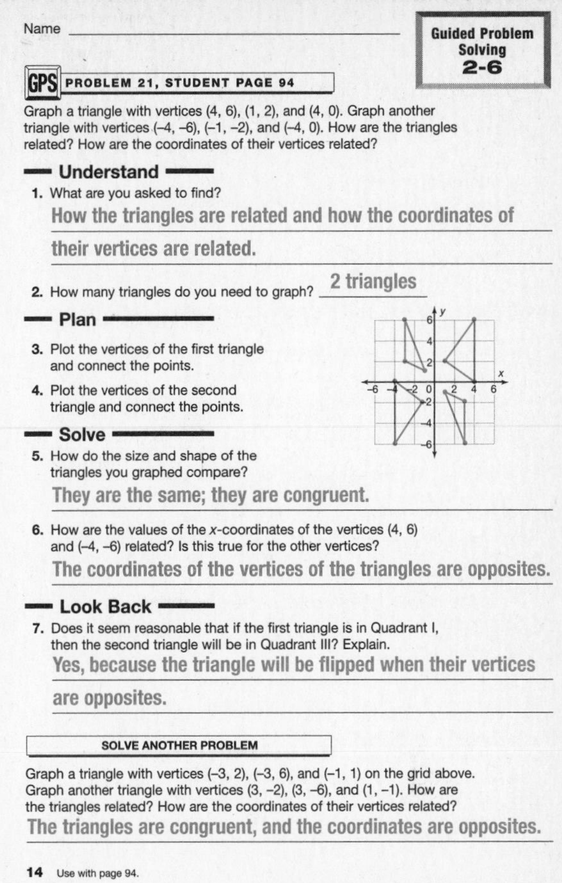

Name ______________________

Guided Problem Solving 2-6

GPS PROBLEM 21, STUDENT PAGE 94

Graph a triangle with vertices (4, 6), (1, 2), and (4, 0). Graph another triangle with vertices (–4, –6), (–1, –2), and (–4, 0). How are the triangles related? How are the coordinates of their vertices related?

Understand

1. What are you asked to find?
 How the triangles are related and how the coordinates of their vertices are related.
2. How many triangles do you need to graph? 2 triangles

Plan

3. Plot the vertices of the first triangle and connect the points.
4. Plot the vertices of the second triangle and connect the points.

Solve

5. How do the size and shape of the triangles you graphed compare?
 They are the same; they are congruent.
6. How are the values of the x-coordinates of the vertices (4, 6) and (–4, –6) related? Is this true for the other vertices?
 The coordinates of the vertices of the triangles are opposites.

Look Back

7. Does it seem reasonable that if the first triangle is in Quadrant I, then the second triangle will be in Quadrant III? Explain.
 Yes, because the triangle will be flipped when their vertices are opposites.

SOLVE ANOTHER PROBLEM

Graph a triangle with vertices (–3, 2), (–3, 6), and (–1, 1) on the grid above. Graph another triangle with vertices (3, –2), (3, –6), and (1, –1). How are the triangles related? How are the coordinates of their vertices related?

The triangles are congruent, and the coordinates are opposites.

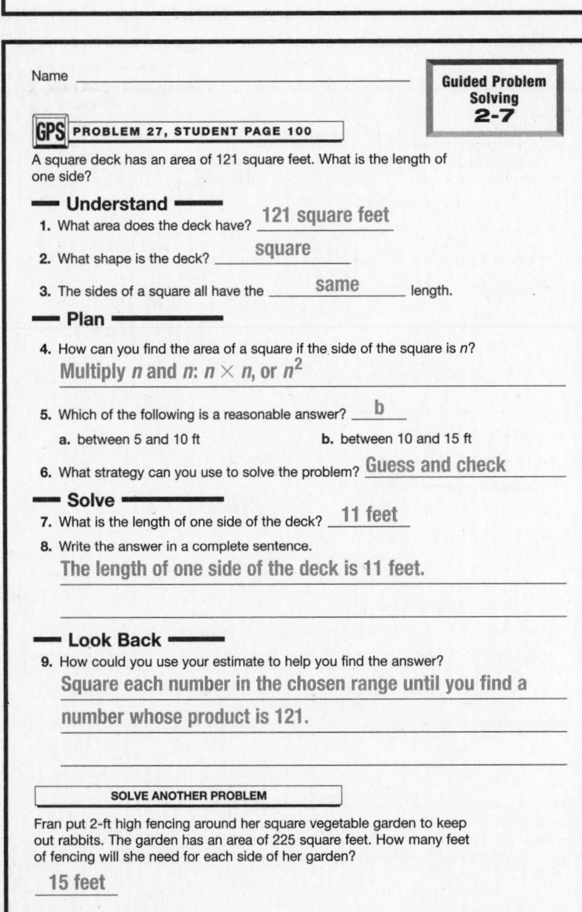

Name ______________________

Guided Problem Solving 2-7

GPS PROBLEM 27, STUDENT PAGE 100

A square deck has an area of 121 square feet. What is the length of one side?

Understand

1. What area does the deck have? 121 square feet
2. What shape is the deck? square
3. The sides of a square all have the same length.

Plan

4. How can you find the area of a square if the side of the square is n?
 Multiply n and n: $n \times n$, or n^2
5. Which of the following is a reasonable answer? b

 a. between 5 and 10 ft b. between 10 and 15 ft

6. What strategy can you use to solve the problem? Guess and check

Solve

7. What is the length of one side of the deck? 11 feet
8. Write the answer in a complete sentence.
 The length of one side of the deck is 11 feet.

Look Back

9. How could you use your estimate to help you find the answer?
 Square each number in the chosen range until you find a number whose product is 121.

SOLVE ANOTHER PROBLEM

Fran put 2-ft high fencing around her square vegetable garden to keep out rabbits. The garden has an area of 225 square feet. How many feet of fencing will she need for each side of her garden?

15 feet

Name ______________________

Guided Problem Solving 2-8

GPS PROBLEM 19, STUDENT PAGE 105

A Russian cosmonaut spent 439 days in space, returning to the earth in March of 1995.

a. How many hours did he spend in space? Write your answer in standard notation.

b. How many minutes did he spend in space? Write this answer in scientific notation.

Understand

1. What are you asked to do? Find the number of hours and minutes in 439 days.

Plan

2. How can you find how many hours are in
 a. 2 days? 2×24 b. 439 days 439×24
3. How can you find how many minutes are in
 a. 2 days? $2(60 \times 24)$ b. 439 days $439(60 \times 24)$

Solve

4. How many hours did the cosmonaut spend in space? 10,536 hours
5. How many minutes did the cosmonaut spend in space? 632,160 minutes
6. Write the number of minutes in scientific notation. 6.3216×10^5

Look Back

7. Why did you write the number of minutes in standard notation before writing it in scientific notation?
 Because the operations used to find the answer were performed on numbers written in standard notation; therefore, only one conversion needed to be done.

SOLVE ANOTHER PROBLEM

Kate's birthday is February 29. She was born in a leap year.

a. How many days does she have to wait between birthdays? Write this answer in standard notation. 1460

b. How many minutes does she have to wait between birthdays? Write this answer in scientific notation. 2.1024×10^6

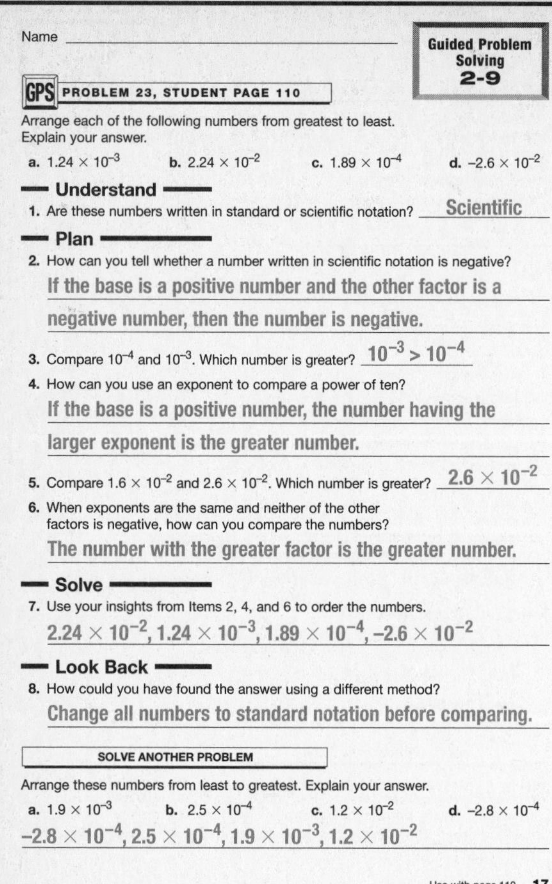

Name ______________________

Guided Problem Solving 2-9

GPS **PROBLEM 23, STUDENT PAGE 110**

Arrange each of the following numbers from greatest to least. Explain your answer.

a. 1.24×10^{-3} **b.** 2.24×10^{-2} **c.** 1.89×10^{-4} **d.** -2.6×10^{-2}

— Understand —

1. Are these numbers written in standard or scientific notation? Scientific

— Plan —

2. How can you tell whether a number written in scientific notation is negative? If the base is a positive number and the other factor is a negative number, then the number is negative.
3. Compare 10^{-4} and 10^{-3}. Which number is greater? $10^{-3} > 10^{-4}$
4. How can you use an exponent to compare a power of ten? If the base is a positive number, the number having the larger exponent is the greater number.
5. Compare 1.6×10^{-2} and 2.6×10^{-2}. Which number is greater? 2.6×10^{-2}
6. When exponents are the same and neither of the other factors is negative, how can you compare the numbers? The number with the greater factor is the greater number.

— Solve —

7. Use your insights from Items 2, 4, and 6 to order the numbers. 2.24×10^{-2}, 1.24×10^{-3}, 1.89×10^{-4}, -2.6×10^{-2}

— Look Back —

8. How could you have found the answer using a different method? Change all numbers to standard notation before comparing.

SOLVE ANOTHER PROBLEM

Arrange these numbers from least to greatest. Explain your answer.

a. 1.9×10^{-3} **b.** 2.5×10^{-4} **c.** 1.2×10^{-2} **d.** -2.8×10^{-4}

-2.8×10^{-4}, 2.5×10^{-4}, 1.9×10^{-3}, 1.2×10^{-2}

Use with page 110. 17

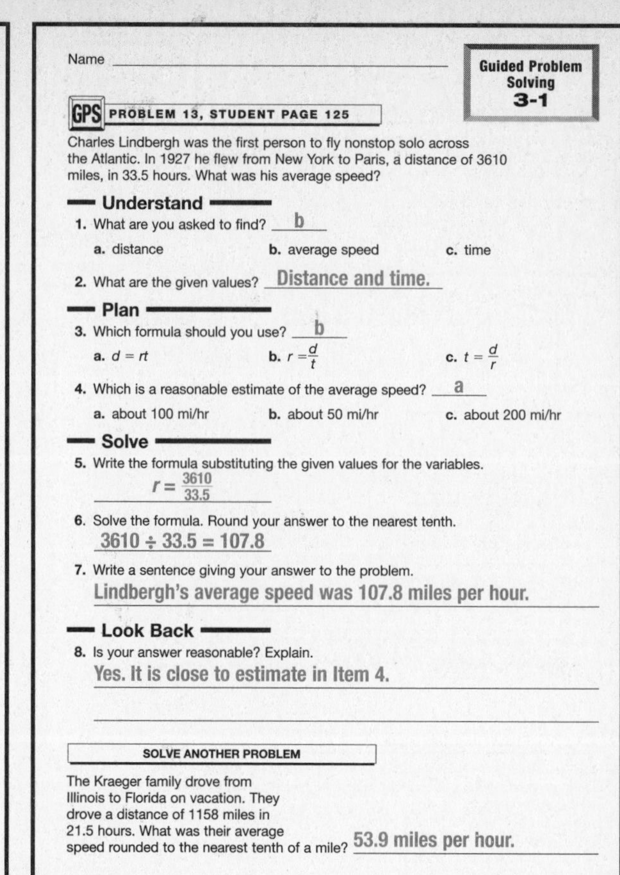

Name ______________________

Guided Problem Solving 3-1

GPS **PROBLEM 13, STUDENT PAGE 125**

Charles Lindbergh was the first person to fly nonstop solo across the Atlantic. In 1927 he flew from New York to Paris, a distance of 3610 miles, in 33.5 hours. What was his average speed?

— Understand —

1. What are you asked to find? b

   a. distance **b.** average speed **c.** time
2. What are the given values? Distance and time.

— Plan —

3. Which formula should you use? b

   a. $d = rt$ **b.** $r = \frac{d}{t}$ **c.** $t = \frac{d}{r}$
4. Which is a reasonable estimate of the average speed? a

   a. about 100 mi/hr **b.** about 50 mi/hr **c.** about 200 mi/hr

— Solve —

5. Write the formula substituting the given values for the variables. $r = \frac{3610}{33.5}$
6. Solve the formula. Round your answer to the nearest tenth. $3610 \div 33.5 = 107.8$
7. Write a sentence giving your answer to the problem. Lindbergh's average speed was 107.8 miles per hour.

— Look Back —

8. Is your answer reasonable? Explain. Yes. It is close to estimate in Item 4.

SOLVE ANOTHER PROBLEM

The Kraeger family drove from Illinois to Florida on vacation. They drove a distance of 1158 miles in 21.5 hours. What was their average speed rounded to the nearest tenth of a mile? 53.9 miles per hour.

18 Use with page 125.

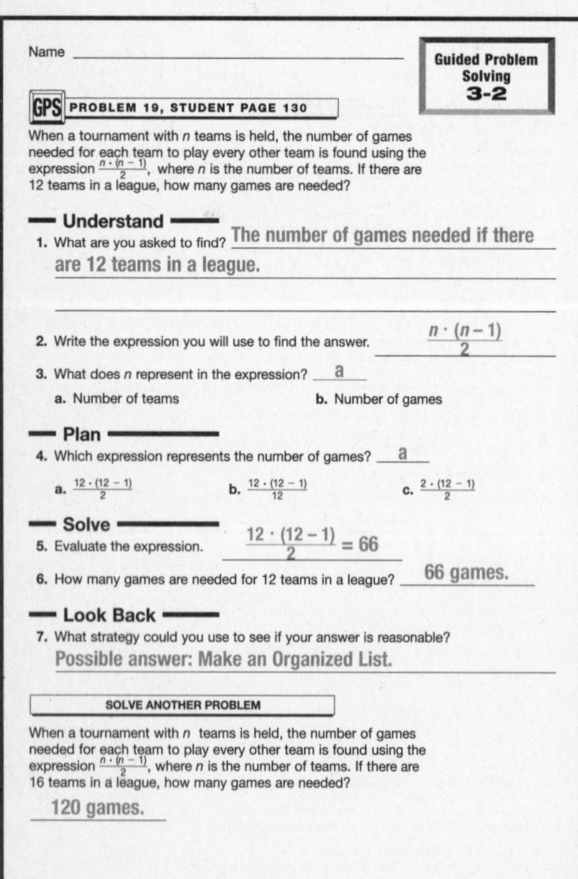

Name ______________________

Guided Problem Solving 3-2

GPS **PROBLEM 19, STUDENT PAGE 130**

When a tournament with n teams is held, the number of games needed for each team to play every other team is found using the expression $\frac{n \cdot (n-1)}{2}$, where n is the number of teams. If there are 12 teams in a league, how many games are needed?

— Understand —

1. What are you asked to find? The number of games needed if there are 12 teams in a league.
2. Write the expression you will use to find the answer. $\frac{n \cdot (n-1)}{2}$
3. What does n represent in the expression? a

   a. Number of teams **b.** Number of games

— Plan —

4. Which expression represents the number of games? a

   a. $\frac{12 \cdot (12-1)}{2}$ **b.** $\frac{12 \cdot (12-1)}{12}$ **c.** $\frac{2 \cdot (12-1)}{2}$

— Solve —

5. Evaluate the expression. $\frac{12 \cdot (12-1)}{2} = 66$
6. How many games are needed for 12 teams in a league? 66 games.

— Look Back —

7. What strategy could you use to see if your answer is reasonable? Possible answer: Make an Organized List.

SOLVE ANOTHER PROBLEM

When a tournament with n teams is held, the number of games needed for each team to play every other team is found using the expression $\frac{n \cdot (n-1)}{2}$, where n is the number of teams. If there are 16 teams in a league, how many games are needed?

120 games.

Use with page 130. 19

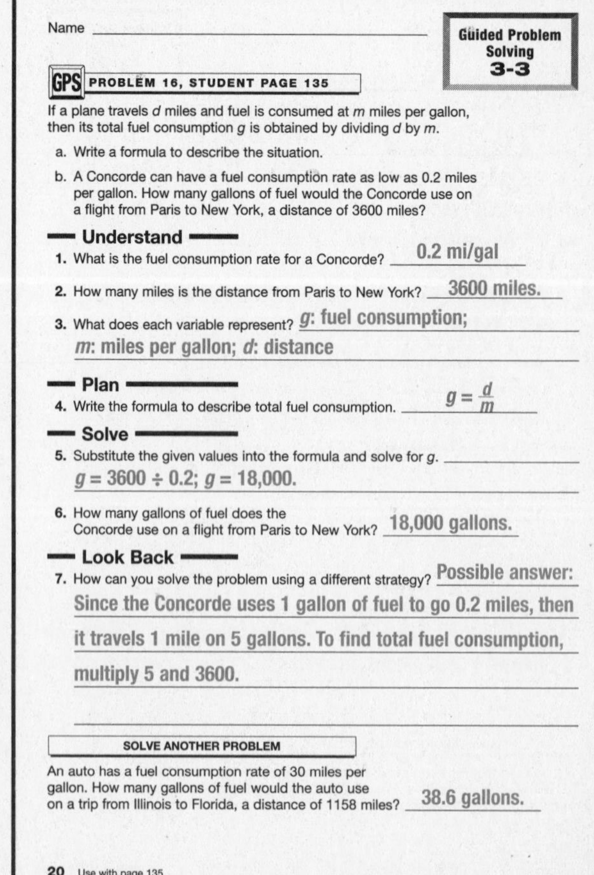

Name ______________________

Guided Problem Solving 3-3

GPS **PROBLEM 16, STUDENT PAGE 135**

If a plane travels d miles and fuel is consumed at m miles per gallon, then its total fuel consumption g is obtained by dividing d by m.

a. Write a formula to describe the situation.

b. A Concorde can have a fuel consumption rate as low as 0.2 miles per gallon. How many gallons of fuel would the Concorde use on a flight from Paris to New York, a distance of 3600 miles?

— Understand —

1. What is the fuel consumption rate for a Concorde? 0.2 mi/gal
2. How many miles is the distance from Paris to New York? 3600 miles.
3. What does each variable represent? g: fuel consumption; m: miles per gallon; d: distance

— Plan —

4. Write the formula to describe total fuel consumption. $g = \frac{d}{m}$

— Solve —

5. Substitute the given values into the formula and solve for g. $g = 3600 \div 0.2$; $g = 18{,}000$.
6. How many gallons of fuel does the Concorde use on a flight from Paris to New York? 18,000 gallons.

— Look Back —

7. How can you solve the problem using a different strategy? Possible answer: Since the Concorde uses 1 gallon of fuel to go 0.2 miles, then it travels 1 mile on 5 gallons. To find total fuel consumption, multiply 5 and 3600.

SOLVE ANOTHER PROBLEM

An auto has a fuel consumption rate of 30 miles per gallon. How many gallons of fuel would the auto use on a trip from Illinois to Florida, a distance of 1158 miles? 38.6 gallons.

20 Use with page 135.

Name ____________________

Guided Problem Solving 3-4

GPS **PROBLEM 23, STUDENT PAGE 143**

A three-way light bulb has three different wattages available as you turn the switch three times in the same direction. The highest wattage is obtained by adding the two lower wattages. If the lowest wattage is 30 watts and the highest wattage is 100 watts, find the middle wattage.

Understand

1. What is the highest wattage? The lowest wattage? 100 watts, 30 watts
2. How is the highest wattage obtained? Find the sum of the lowest and the middle wattages.

Plan

3. Which of the following would be a range within which the answer falls? c
   a. Between 0-30 watts b. Between 130-200 watts c. Between 30 and 100 watts
4. Let w represent the middle wattage. Then choose the equation that best represents the situation. b
   a. $w = 100 + 30$ b. $w + 30 = 100$ c. $w - 100 = 30$

Solve

6. Solve your chosen equation. $w = 70$
7. What is the middle wattage? 70 watts.

Look Back

8. How do you know your answer is reasonable? Possible answer: The middle wattage falls between the highest and lowest wattages. Since $30 < 70 < 100$, it is reasonable.

SOLVE ANOTHER PROBLEM

The highest wattage on a three-way light bulb is obtained by adding the two lower wattages. If the lowest wattage is 50 watts and the highest wattage is 250 watts, find the middle wattage. 200 watts.

Name ____________________

Guided Problem Solving 3-5

GPS **PROBLEM 30, STUDENT PAGE 149**

An appliance that uses 1000 watts of power in 1 hour uses 1 kilowatt-hour (1 kWh) of energy. (Note that *kilo* means 1000.) Most electric companies charge by the kilowatt-hour. An appliance that uses 200 watts per hour for 5 hours also uses 1 kilowatt-hour of energy. Suppose a family uses 500 kWh in one month and they are charged $45. What is the cost per kWh?

Understand

1. How many kilowatt-hours were used in a month? 500 kilowatt-hours
2. How much was the family charged for the month? $45
3. What are you asked to find? Cost per kilowatt-hour.

Plan

4. Let c represent the cost per kWh. Then choose the equation that represents the situation. a
   a. $500c = 45$ b. $45c = 500$ c. $c + 45 = 500$
5. Describe how you can isolate the variable and solve the equation. Divide both sides of the equation by 500.

Solve

6. Solve the equation you chose in Item 4. $c =$ 0.09
7. Write a sentence to give the cost per kWh. The cost per kilowatt-hour is $0.09.

Look Back

8. How can you check your answer? Possible answer: Substitute the value for c into the equation to see if the equation is true.

SOLVE ANOTHER PROBLEM

A family's electric bill one month showed 1400 kWh were used. The total charges were $196. What was the cost per kWh? $0.14

Name ____________________

Guided Problem Solving 3-6

GPS **PROBLEM 30, STUDENT PAGE 154**

A paging service charges $20.00 for activation plus $12.95 a month. Francine paid $123.60 for activation and service. How many months did this cover?

Understand

1. How much does the paging service charge per month? $12.95
2. How much was the activation fee? $20.00
3. How much did Francine pay for activation and service? $123.60

Plan

4. Let m represent the number of months covered by $123.60. Then choose the equation that represents the situation. c
   a. $20m = 123.60$ b. $12.95 + m = 123.60$ c. $20 + 12.95m = 123.60$
5. Which operation will you undo first? c
   a. Multiplication b. Subtraction c. Addition

Solve

7. Solve the equation you chose in Item 4. $m = 8$
8. Write a sentence to give the final answer. The money Francine paid covers 8 months of service.

Look Back

9. How can you determine if your answer is reasonable? Possible answer: Use front-end estimation and compare the estimate [$20 + 10m = 100$, $m = 8$] to the actual answer to see if they are close.

SOLVE ANOTHER PROBLEM

Parking garage fees are $3 plus $1.50 per hour. If the total parking fee was $16.50, how many hours was the car parked? 9 hours.

Name ____________________

Guided Problem Solving 3-7

GPS **PROBLEM 30, STUDENT PAGE 159**

You have made scores of (75) and (82) on your first two tests in Spanish. What scores can you get on your next test if you want to maintain an average of at least 80?

Understand

1. Circle the test scores you have already made.
2. What average do you want to maintain? At least 80.

Plan

3. Which operations do you use to find an average? b
   a. Addition, subtraction b. Addition, division c. Multiplication, division
4. Let x represent the score on your next test. Which inequality represents the average of the test scores? b
   a. $\frac{x + 75 + 82}{3} > 80$ b. $\frac{x + 75 + 82}{3} \geq 80$ c. $\frac{x + 75 + 82}{3} \leq 80$

Solve

5. Solve the inequality chosen in Item 4. $x \geq 83$
6. What score can you get on your next test to maintain an average of at least 80? A score of 83 or higher.

Look Back

7. You know that 75 is 5 less than the desired average and 82 is 2 greater than the desired average. How can this help you find the scores you need to get on your next test using mental math? Possible answer: Add 5 to 80 and then subtract 2. ($80 + 5 - 2 = 83$) So, one needs a score of 83 or higher.

SOLVE ANOTHER PROBLEM

Your quiz scores are 85 and 91 in Social Studies. If you want to maintain an average of at least 90, what scores can you get on your next quiz? A score of 94 or higher.

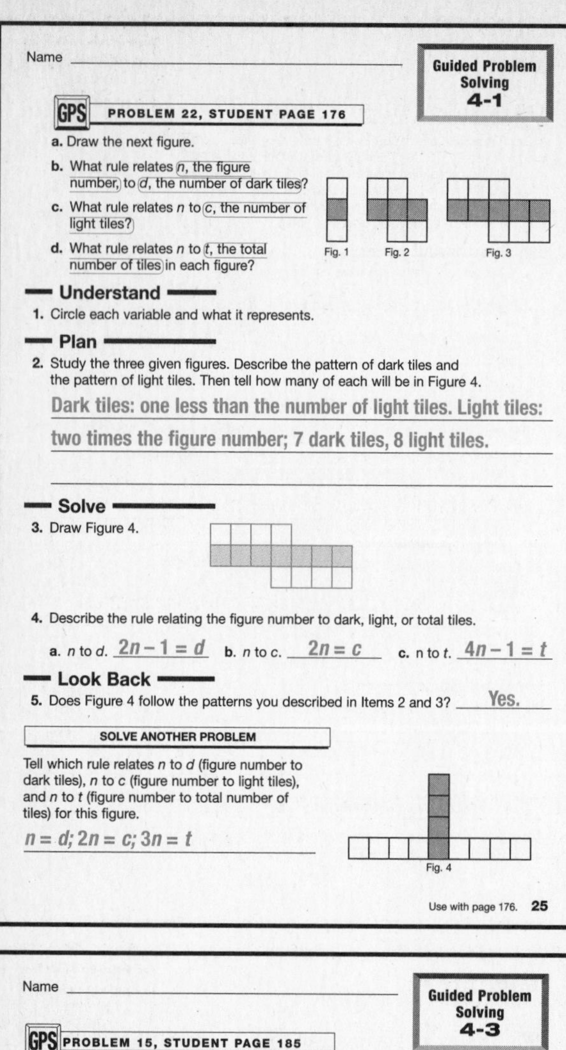

Name ______________________

Guided Problem Solving 4-1

GPS PROBLEM 22, STUDENT PAGE 176

a. Draw the next figure.

b. What rule relates n, the figure number, to d, the number of dark tiles?

c. What rule relates n to c, the number of light tiles?

d. What rule relates n to t, the total number of tiles in each figure?

Fig. 1 Fig. 2 Fig. 3

Understand

1. Circle each variable and what it represents.

Plan

2. Study the three given figures. Describe the pattern of dark tiles and the pattern of light tiles. Then tell how many of each will be in Figure 4.
Dark tiles: one less than the number of light tiles. Light tiles: two times the figure number; 7 dark tiles, 8 light tiles.

Solve

3. Draw Figure 4.

4. Describe the rule relating the figure number to dark, light, or total tiles.
a. n to d. $2n - 1 = d$ b. n to c. $2n = c$ c. n to t. $4n - 1 = t$

Look Back

5. Does Figure 4 follow the patterns you described in Items 2 and 3? Yes.

SOLVE ANOTHER PROBLEM

Tell which rule relates n to d (figure number to dark tiles), n to c (figure number to light tiles), and n to t (figure number to total number of tiles) for this figure.

$n = d$; $2n = c$; $3n = t$

Fig. 4

Use with page 176. 25

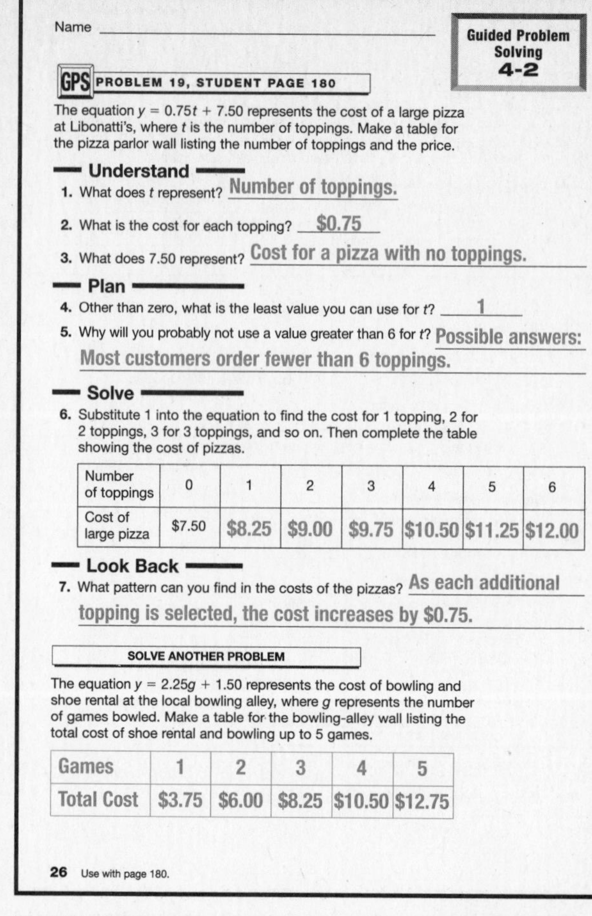

Name ______________________

Guided Problem Solving 4-2

GPS PROBLEM 19, STUDENT PAGE 180

The equation $y = 0.75t + 7.50$ represents the cost of a large pizza at Libonatti's, where t is the number of toppings. Make a table for the pizza parlor wall listing the number of toppings and the price.

Understand

1. What does t represent? Number of toppings.

2. What is the cost for each topping? $0.75

3. What does 7.50 represent? Cost for a pizza with no toppings.

Plan

4. Other than zero, what is the least value you can use for t? 1

5. Why will you probably not use a value greater than 6 for t? Possible answers: Most customers order fewer than 6 toppings.

Solve

6. Substitute 1 into the equation to find the cost for 1 topping, 2 for 2 toppings, 3 for 3 toppings, and so on. Then complete the table showing the cost of pizzas.

Number of toppings	0	1	2	3	4	5	6
Cost of large pizza	$7.50	$8.25	$9.00	$9.75	$10.50	$11.25	$12.00

Look Back

7. What pattern can you find in the costs of the pizzas? As each additional topping is selected, the cost increases by $0.75.

SOLVE ANOTHER PROBLEM

The equation $y = 2.25g + 1.50$ represents the cost of bowling and shoe rental at the local bowling alley, where g represents the number of games bowled. Make a table for the bowling-alley wall listing the total cost of shoe rental and bowling up to 5 games.

Games	1	2	3	4	5
Total Cost	$3.75	$6.00	$8.25	$10.50	$12.75

26 Use with page 180.

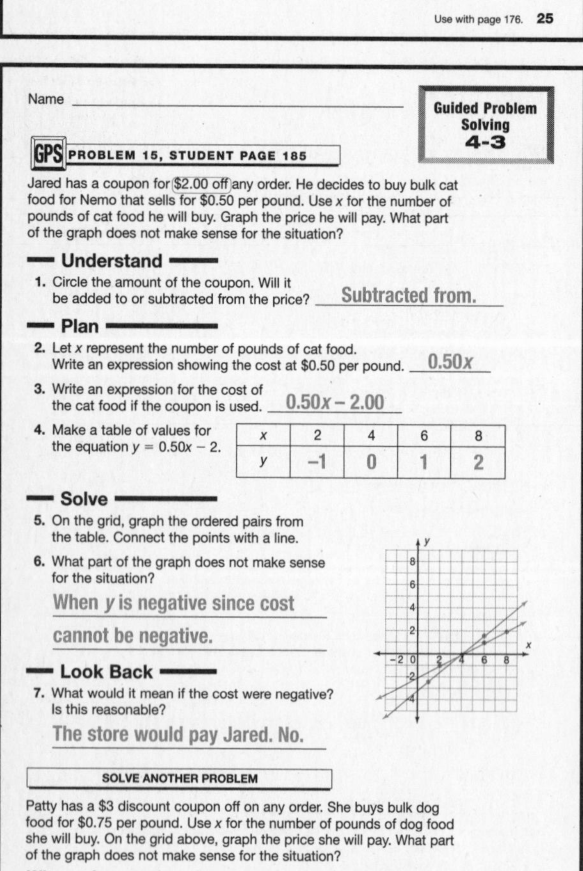

Name ______________________

Guided Problem Solving 4-3

GPS PROBLEM 15, STUDENT PAGE 185

Jared has a coupon for $2.00 off any order. He decides to buy bulk cat food for Nemo that sells for $0.50 per pound. Use x for the number of pounds of cat food he will buy. Graph the price he will pay. What part of the graph does not make sense for the situation?

Understand

1. Circle the amount of the coupon. Will it be added to or subtracted from the price? Subtracted from.

Plan

2. Let x represent the number of pounds of cat food. Write an expression showing the cost at $0.50 per pound. $0.50x$

3. Write an expression for the cost of the cat food if the coupon is used. $0.50x - 2.00$

4. Make a table of values for the equation $y = 0.50x - 2$.

x	2	4	6	8
y	−1	0	1	2

Solve

5. On the grid, graph the ordered pairs from the table. Connect the points with a line.

6. What part of the graph does not make sense for the situation? When y is negative since cost cannot be negative.

Look Back

7. What would it mean if the cost were negative? Is this reasonable? The store would pay Jared. No.

SOLVE ANOTHER PROBLEM

Patty has a $3 discount coupon off on any order. She buys bulk dog food for $0.75 per pound. Use x for the number of pounds of dog food she will buy. On the grid above, graph the price she will pay. What part of the graph does not make sense for the situation?

When y is negative since cost cannot be negative.

Use with page 185. 27

Name ______________________

Guided Problem Solving 4-4

GPS PROBLEM 15, STUDENT PAGE 193

A wheelchair ramp is allowed a maximum of one inch of rise for every foot of run. Express this slope as a fraction. (Hint: Use the same units.)

Understand

1. What is the rise? One inch.

2. What is the run? One foot.

3. How are you to write the slope? As a fraction.

Plan

4. Choose the correct definition. The slope is a
a. rise divided by the run. b. run divided by the rise.

5. If you express each measure in inches, what will you use for the rise and run?
a. Rise 1 in. b. Run 12 in.

Solve

6. Write the slope of the ramp. $\frac{1}{12}$

7. Write a sentence to give the final answer.
The slope of the wheelchair ramp is $\frac{1}{12}$.

Look Back

8. How can you find the answer using feet as the unit of measure?
$\frac{\frac{1}{12}}{1} = \frac{1}{12}$

SOLVE ANOTHER PROBLEM

A boat ramp has no more than four inches of rise for every three feet of run. Express this slope as a fraction. (Hint: Use the same units.)

$\frac{4\text{ in.}}{3\text{ft}} = \frac{4\text{ in.}}{36\text{ in.}} = \frac{1}{9}$

28 Use with page 193.

Name ____________________

Guided Problem Solving 4-5

GPS PROBLEM 19, STUDENT PAGE 199

Marty belongs to a swim club. With a membership fee of $20 per year, the members can swim any number of times for a reduced rate of $2 per swim. Make a graph to show the total cost for varying numbers of swims. Explain how to find a typical cost from the graph.

Understand

1. How much is the membership fee? $20 per year.
2. How much does it cost each time Marty swims? $2

Plan

3. Write an equation. Let x = the number of times Marty swims and y = the total cost. $y = 2x + 20$
4. Make a table of ordered pairs for x and y. Possible answers:

x	1	2	3	4
y	22	24	26	28

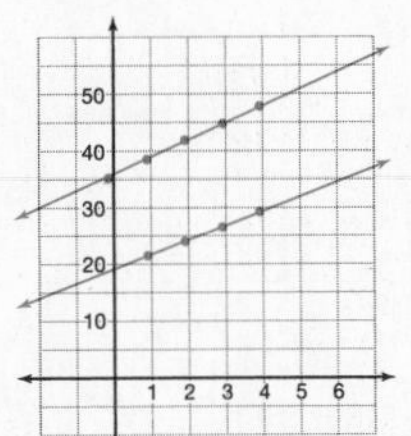

Solve

5. Graph the points on the grid.
6. Explain how to find a typical cost from the graph.
   Find the point directly above the desired number of times and read the label at the left to find the cost.

Look Back

7. What part of the graph does not make sense for the situation?
   When the value of x is negative.

SOLVE ANOTHER PROBLEM Possible answers: shown on grid above.

John pays $35 each year for a zoo membership. As a member, he pays only a $3 parking fee each time he visits the zoo. On the grid above, graph the total cost for varying numbers of zoo visits.

Name ____________________

Guided Problem Solving 4-6

GPS PROBLEM 15, STUDENT PAGE 205

Which would be less expensive for 12 tickets, buying a weekend ski lift pass for $30.00 plus $1.50 per lift or just paying $4.00 per lift?

Understand

1. How many tickets will be purchased? 12 tickets.
2. How many different choices are there for buying the tickets? 2 choices.

Plan

3. How can you find the cost of 12 tickets at $1.50 each plus $30 for a pass?
   Multiply 12 and 1.50; then add 30.
4. How can you find the cost of 12 tickets at $4 each? Multiply 12 and 4.
5. How can you decide which is less expensive? Compare answers.

Solve

6. Find the cost of 12 tickets at $1.50 each plus $30 for a pass. $48
7. Find the cost of 12 tickets at $4 each. $48
8. Which method represents the less expensive way to buy 12 tickets?
   Both answers represent the same price.

Look Back

9. If you buy more than or less than 12 tickets, will both ways to buy tickets cost the same amount of money? Explain.
   No; the ski pass is less expensive for more than 12 tickets and more expensive for fewer than 12 tickets.

SOLVE ANOTHER PROBLEM

Which would be less expensive for 15 games at the carnival, paying an admission of $5 plus $1.50 for each game or buying game tokens for $2 each?
Paying $5 admission plus $1.50 for each game.

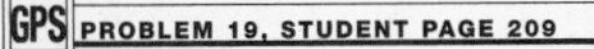

Name ____________________

Guided Problem Solving 4-7

GPS PROBLEM 19, STUDENT PAGE 209

The Environment Club will have a party if the students collect at least 3.5 pounds of recyclable aluminum cans per student within a month. Graph the number of pounds (P) that must be collected by n students.

Understand

1. What is the least number of pounds of aluminum cans that needs to be collected per student? 3.5 pounds.
2. What does the variable P stand for? Total number of pounds.
3. What does the variable n stand for? Number of students.

Plan

4. Write an equation using the variables. $P = 3.5n$
5. Since students can collect as much as or more than 3.5 pounds of cans per student, write an inequality using ≥. $P \geq 3.5n$
6. Make a table of values for $P = 3.5n$.

n	0	2	4	6
P	0	7	14	21

Solve

7. Use a solid line to graph the equation $P = 3.5n$.
8. Choose a point not on the line and substitute the ordered pair into the inequality. Shade one section of the graph.

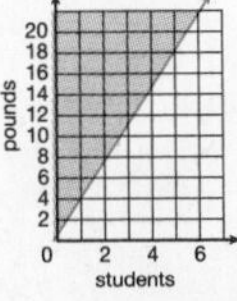

Look Back

9. How can you tell if you shaded the correct section on your graph? Explain.
   If the inequality is true, shade the side of the graph containing the point. If not, shade the other side.

SOLVE ANOTHER PROBLEM

The scout troop will go camping if the troop sells at least 12 boxes of cookies per scout. On another sheet of paper, graph the number of boxes (B) that must be sold by x scouts.

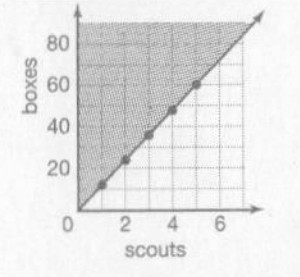

Name ____________________

Guided Problem Solving 5-1

GPS PROBLEM 5, STUDENT PAGE 225

A modem originally priced at $200 is on sale for $129. A faster modem priced at $350 is on sale for $249. Is the ratio of the sale price to the original price the same?

Understand

1. How many modems are on sale? 2 modems.
2. What ratio do you need to find for each modem?
   Sale price to original price.

Plan

3. Write the ratio for the first modem. $\frac{129}{200}$
4. Write the ratio for the faster modem. $\frac{249}{350}$
5. How can you compare the ratios for each modem?
   Divide each sale price by its original price; then compare the decimals.

Solve

6. For the ratio $\frac{129}{200}$, divide 129 by 200. 0.645
7. For the ratio $\frac{249}{350}$, divide 249 by 350. 0.7114286
8. Compare results for the ratios in Items 6 and 7. Are they the same? No.
9. Is the ratio of the sale price to the original price the same? No.

Look Back

10. Describe how you can compare the ratios using fractions rather than decimals.
    Possible answer: Write ratios as fractions with the same denominators; then compare the numerators.

SOLVE ANOTHER PROBLEM

An office-supply catalog has 10 packs of computer diskettes selling for $7.99 with a list price of $18.00. The catalog also sells 25 packs of diskettes for $18.99 with a list price of $38.00. Is the ratio of the selling price to the list price the same? No.

Name ______________________

Guided Problem Solving 5-2

GPS PROBLEM 16, STUDENT PAGE 231

If phone calls are 30¢ per minute and are billed in 6-sec (0.1 min) increments, make an equal ratio table with at least six entries.

Understand

1. What is the charge per minute? 30¢ per minute.
2. How many seconds are in each billed increment? 6 seconds.
3. What do you need to make? An equal ratio table.
4. How many entries do you need to find for the table? At least six.

Plan

5. What is the given ratio for the equal ratio table? 30¢:1 min
6. What will you label the two rows of the equal ratio table?
   Cost and Minutes.
7. How will you find equal ratios to the left of 30¢:1 min in the table?
   Possible answer: Divide by $\frac{2}{2}, \frac{5}{5}, \frac{10}{10}$.
8. How will you find equal ratios to the right of 30¢:1 min in the table?
   Possible answer: Multiply by $\frac{2}{2}, \frac{3}{3}$.

Solve

9. Complete the table to find 6 ratios equal to 30¢:1 min.

Cost (¢)	3	6	15	30	60	90
Minutes	0.1	0.2	0.5	1	2	3

Look Back

10. How can you be sure all the ratios are equal? Find cross products.

SOLVE ANOTHER PROBLEM

One long-distance phone company offered a special weekend rate of 15¢ per minute. The billing was in 20-second ($\frac{1}{3}$ minute) increments. Make an equal ratio table with at least six entries. Possible answer:

Cost (¢)	5	10	15	30	45	60
Minutes	$\frac{1}{3}$	$\frac{2}{3}$	1	2	3	4

Name ______________________

Guided Problem Solving 5-3

GPS PROBLEM 13, STUDENT PAGE 238

Make a graph of downloading times to show that downloading a 900K file in 6 min is the same rate as downloading a 225K file in 1.5 min.

Understand

1. Circle both rates.
2. What are you asked to make? A graph.

Plan

3. Which part of the ratio will you graph on the x-axis? a
   a. The time in minutes b. The size of the file
4. Name the ordered pairs. (6, 900) (1.5, 225)

Solve

5. Complete the graph. Label the x-axis with time in minutes and the y-axis with file size.

File size (K): 200, 400, 600, 800, 1000
Time (min): 1, 2, 3, 4, 5, 6

Look Back

6. Why does your graph show that the rates are the same? Because the line through the two points passes through the origin.

SOLVE ANOTHER PROBLEM

Make a graph of ticket costs to show that $60 for 5 admission tickets is the same rate as $24 for 2 tickets.

Cost ($): 10, 20, 30, 40, 50, 60, 70
Number of tickets: 1, 2, 3, 4, 5, 6

Name ______________________

Guided Problem Solving 5-4

GPS PROBLEM 31, STUDENT PAGE 246

The lengths of the sides of a triangle are in a ratio of 6:5:3. The triangle's perimeter is 56 cm. What is the length of each side?

Understand

1. What is the ratio of the lengths of the sides of the triangle? 6:5:3
2. What is the perimeter of the triangle? 56 centimeters.
3. What are you asked to find? Length of each side.

Plan

4. How do you find the perimeter of a triangle? Add lengths of sides.
5. What is the sum of the given ratios? 14
6. Divide the perimeter by the sum of the ratios. 4

Solve

7. Multiply each number in the ratio by your answer in Item 6 to find the lengths of the sides.
   24 cm, 20 cm, and 12 cm
8. Write a sentence that answers the question to the problem.
   Possible answer: The lengths are 24 cm, 20 cm, and 12 cm.

Look Back

9. What other strategies can you use to solve the problem?
   Possible answers: Guess and Check, Make a Table.

SOLVE ANOTHER PROBLEM

The lengths of the sides of a triangle are in a ratio of 5:4:3. The triangle's perimeter is 84 cm. What is the length of each side?

The lengths of the sides are 35 cm, 28 cm, and 21 cm.

Name ______________________

Guided Problem Solving 5-5

GPS PROBLEM 13, STUDENT PAGE 250

Which is the better buy: a 16-oz box of cereal for $3.49 or a 6-oz box of cereal for $1.25?

Understand

1. How many sizes of boxes are you comparing? 2 sizes.
2. What do you need to find for each box size? Cost per ounce.

Plan

3. Write the ratio $\frac{\text{cost}}{\text{ounces}}$ for each box size. $\frac{3.49}{16}, \frac{1.25}{6}$
4. Do you multiply or divide to find the unit rate for each box? Divide.

Solve

5. Find the unit rate for the 16-oz box of cereal. Round your answer to the nearest cent. $0.22
6. Find the unit rate for the 6-oz box of cereal. Round your answer to the nearest cent. $0.21
7. Write a sentence that tells which product is the better buy.
   The 6-oz box of cereal is a better buy.

Look Back

8. How can you check your answer?
   Possible answer: Recalculate the unit rates and compare to see if your results are the same.

SOLVE ANOTHER PROBLEM

Which is the better buy: a 4.6-oz tube of toothpaste for $1.89 or a 6.4-oz tube for $2.29? Give the unit rates to support your answer.

The 6.4-oz tube is the better buy; 4.6-oz tube: $0.41 to nearest cent; 6.4-oz tube: $0.36 to nearest cent.

Name ______

Guided Problem Solving 5-6

GPS **PROBLEM 4, STUDENT PAGE 254**

In a movie, large sets are often created so that people appear to be smaller. If a 60-in. tall person appears next to a 96-in. high trash can, but the trash can appears to be 18 in. high in the film, how tall would the person appear to be?

Understand

1. What will the 60-inch tall person stand next to? A 96-in. tall trash can.
2. How tall will the trash can appear in the film? 18 in.
3. Will the person be larger or smaller than the trash can in the film? Smaller.
4. What do you need to find? Height of person in film.

Plan

5. Which ratio compares the actual height of the person to actual height of the trash can? a

   a. $\frac{60}{96}$ b. $\frac{96}{60}$ c. $\frac{60}{18}$
6. Let x represent the height of the person in the film. Which ratio compares the height of the person to the height of the trash can in the film? c

   a. $\frac{18}{x}$ b. $\frac{x}{96}$ c. $\frac{x}{18}$

Solve

7. Write a proportion using the equal ratios representing the height of the person to the height of the trash can. $\frac{60}{96} = \frac{x}{18}$
8. Solve the proportion for x and give the answer. $x =$ 11.25; 11.25 in.

Look Back

9. How can you check to see if your answer is correct?
   Possible answer: Substitute your answer for x. Then write a decimal for both ratios to see if they are equal.

SOLVE ANOTHER PROBLEM

A 48-inch child is sitting in a 84-inch chair. If the chair will appear to be 42 inches high in the film, how tall will the child appear to be? 24 in.

Name ______

Guided Problem Solving 5-7

GPS **PROBLEM 21, STUDENT PAGE 261**

The average NBA player is approximately 6 ft 9 in. tall, and the basket is 10 ft high. The average eighth grader is 5 ft 5 in. tall. How much should the basket be lowered for the eighth graders to make the ratio of player height to basket height the same?

Understand

1. How tall is the average NBA player? 6 ft 9 in.
2. How tall is the average 8th grader? 5 ft 5 in.
3. Should the basket be raised or lowered for the eighth graders? Lowered.

Plan

4. Convert all measurements to inches. Use 1 foot = 12 inches.

   a. 6 ft 9 in. 81 in. b. 5 ft 5 in. 65 in. c. 10 ft 120 in.
5. Write a ratio of the NBA player's height to the basket height. 81:120
6. Let x = the adjusted height of the basket for an eighth grader. Write a ratio of the height for an eighth grader to the adjusted basket height. 65:x

Solve

7. Write the ratios as a proportion and solve for x. $\frac{81}{120} = \frac{65}{x}$; $x = 96.3$
8. To find how much the basket should be lowered, first subtract the value of x from 120. Then write a sentence answering the question.
   23.7; the basket should be lowered 23.7 in.

Look Back

9. How can you estimate to see if your answer is reasonable?
   Eighth grader height is about $\frac{5}{6}$ that of an NBA player. $\frac{5}{6}$ of 120 is 100. 120 − 100 = 20; 20 is close to 23.7.

SOLVE ANOTHER PROBLEM

Suppose the average male height is 5 ft 9 in. What should the height of the basket be to the nearest inch so that player height is proportional to basket height? 102 in.

Name ______

Guided Problem Solving 6-1

GPS **PROBLEM 23, STUDENT PAGE 279**

To make the color light brown, you mix 7 parts red, 2 parts yellow, and 1 part blue. What percent of the light-brown coloring is red? Yellow? Blue?

Understand

1. What are you asked to find? Percent of tan that is red, yellow, blue.
2. How many parts of the color light brown are

   a. red? 7 parts. b. yellow? 2 parts. c. blue? 1 part.

Plan

3. If the parts of the color light brown are written as a fraction, what would
   a. the numerator represent? Part that is red, yellow, or blue.
   b. the denominator represent? Total of red, yellow, and blue parts.
4. How many parts are there in all in the color light brown? 10 parts.

Solve

5. Write the number of red parts as a fraction. $\frac{7}{10}$
6. Write an equivalent fraction with the denominator 100 for the number of red parts. $\frac{70}{100}$
7. Write the percent of the color light brown that is red. 70%
8. Repeat steps 5–7 to find the percent that is yellow. $\frac{2}{10} = \frac{20}{100} = 20\%$
9. Repeat steps 5–7 to find the percent that is blue. $\frac{1}{10} = \frac{10}{100} = 10\%$

Look Back

10. How could you have solved the problem in a different way? Possible answer: Draw and shade a diagram.

SOLVE ANOTHER PROBLEM

There are 10 sixth-graders, 15 seventh-graders, and 25 eighth-graders in the drama club. What percent of the club members are sixth-graders? seventh-graders? eighth-graders?

Sixth: 20%; Seventh: 30%; Eighth: 50%.

Name ______

Guided Problem Solving 6-2

GPS **PROBLEM 14, STUDENT PAGE 284**

A bin contains 120 ears of white and yellow corn. Of these, 78 ears are yellow. What percent of the ears of corn are yellow? What percent are white?

Understand

1. How many ears of corn are in the bin? 120 ears.
2. How many of the ears of corn in the bin are yellow? 78 ears.
3. What are you asked to find? Percent of yellow ears, white ears.

Plan

4. What percent of the corn is made up of both the yellow and the white ears? 100%
5. Which proportion will you use to find the percent of yellow ears? c

   a. $\frac{x}{120} = \frac{78}{100}$ b. $\frac{100}{120} = \frac{78}{x}$ c. $\frac{78}{120} = \frac{x}{100}$
6. Which operation can you use to find the percent of white corn once you know what percent is yellow and the total percent? Subtraction.

Solve

7. Solve your proportion to find the percent of yellow corn. 65%
8. What is the percent of white corn in the bin? 35%

Look Back

9. Check your answer by writing, then solving, an equation to find the percent of *white* corn in the bin.
   $p \cdot 120 = 120 - 78$; $120p = 42$; $p = 0.35 = 35\%$

SOLVE ANOTHER PROBLEM

There are 475 students at Washington Middle School. On the day of the big game, 304 students wore school colors. What percent of the students wore school colors? What percent did not wear school colors?

Wore: 64%; Did not wear: 36%.

Name ______________________

Guided Problem Solving 6-3

GPS PROBLEM 24, STUDENT PAGE 290

The average daily intake of calories is 2000. For a snack, Leandro had yogurt (250 calories) and a small bag of chips (160 calories). Approximately what percent of his total caloric intake did Leandro have at lunch?

Understand

1. How many calories does Leandro consume per day? ≈ 2000 calories.
2. How many calories were in the yogurt? 250 calories.
3. How many calories were in the bag of chips? 160 calories.

Plan

4. Complete the equation to find how many calories were in the snack.

   250 + 160 = 410
5. Write the fraction that shows what part of Leandro's average daily caloric intake was consumed during his snack. $\frac{410}{2000}$

Solve

6. Choose compatible numbers and rewrite the fraction in Item 5. $\frac{400}{2000}$
7. Write the fraction in Item 6 in lowest terms. $\frac{400}{2000} = \frac{1}{5}$
8. About what percent of his daily calories is in Leandro's snack? About 20%.

Look Back

9. How does your answer change if you round to estimate Leandro's caloric intake without compensating for rounding both numbers up?

   Possible answer: The estimated intake increases since the estimated fractional part is $\frac{500}{2000}$, or about 25%.

SOLVE ANOTHER PROBLEM

Monica ate spaghetti and a salad for lunch. She had a total of 450 calories and 15 grams of fat in her meal. Each gram of fat has 9 calories. Approximately what percent of the calories for her lunch came from fat? About 30%.

Name ______________________

Guided Problem Solving 6-4

GPS PROBLEM 20, STUDENT PAGE 299

Suppose you make $20,000 a year and spend 25% of your salary on rent. If your salary increases 10% and your rent increases 5%, what percent of your salary will be spent on housing?

Understand

1. What is your salary? $20,000
2. What percent of your salary is spent on rent? 25%
3. What is the percent increase in salary? 10%
4. What is the percent increase in rent? 5%

Plan

5. Write an equation to find the rent expense *before* any salary or rent increases. $0.25 \cdot 20{,}000 = 5{,}000$
6. Which equation will you use to find your new salary? Let x equal your new salary. b

   a. $x = (20{,}000 \times 100\%) \times 10\%$ **b.** $x = 20{,}000 \times (100\% + 10\%)$

Solve

7. What is your salary *after* the increase? $22,000
8. What is your rent *before* the increase? $5,000
9. What is your rent *after* the increase? $5,250
10. Write the ratio of new rental cost to new salary. $\frac{5{,}250}{22{,}000}$
11. Write the ratio in Item 10 as a percent. Round to the nearest whole number percent. 24%

Look Back

12. Write another equation you could use to find the increased salary.

    $20{,}000 \times 0.10 + 20{,}000 = 2{,}000 + 20{,}000 = 22{,}000$.

SOLVE ANOTHER PROBLEM

Suppose you make $30,000 a year and spend 20% of your salary on rent. If your salary increases 4% and your rent increases 9%, what percent of your salary will be spent on housing? About 21%.

Name ______________________

Guided Problem Solving 6-5

GPS PROBLEM 18, STUDENT PAGE 304

Ellen needs to raise the price of a $10 item and lower the price of a $15 item so they are equal. But she can only enter percent increases and percent decreases in the pricing computer. Give an example of how she can do this.

Understand

1. Underline the current prices of the two items. Possible answers: 4–9
2. Will the two new prices be the same or different amounts? Same.

Plan

3. What range will the new price fall between? a

   a. $10 and $15 **b.** $15 and $20 **c.** $20 and $25
4. Choose a number that falls within the range you chose in Item 4. $11
5. Write an equation to find the percent change between $10 and the price you selected. $11 - 10 = p \cdot 10$
6. Write an equation to find the percent change between $15 and the price you selected. $15 - 11 = p \cdot 15$

Solve

7. What is the percent change between $10 and the new price? Give change as a percent increase or decrease. 10% increase.
8. What is the percent change between $15 and the new price? Give change as a percent increase or decrease. $26\frac{2}{3}$% decrease.

Look Back

9. Could you have chosen a different price for the two items? Explain. Yes, any price in the range. Percent changes would be revised.

SOLVE ANOTHER PROBLEM

Jon needs to lower the prices of a $20 item and a $25 item so they are equal. But he can only enter percent increases and percent decreases in the computer. Give an example of how he can do this. Possible answer: Choose any amount < $20, e.g. $18. Find percents decrease between $20 and $18 (10%), and $25 and $18 (28%).

Name ______________________

Guided Problem Solving 6-6

GPS PROBLEM 23, STUDENT PAGE 310

A store has increased its wholesale prices 60%. What is the greatest percent of discount it can offer during a sale without selling its products below cost?

Understand

1. What percent were the prices originally increased? 60%
2. What are you asked to find? Greatest possible discount that can be given without selling the products below cost.

Plan

3. Will the discount be less than, more than, or equal to 60%? Explain. Less than; since it is calculated on a higher amount, it must be less.
4. Solve a simpler problem by giving one of the products a price. If the wholesale price is $10, what is the current retail price? $16
5. Write an equation to find the percent decrease between the current retail price in Item 4 and $10. $16 - 10 = p \cdot 16$

Solve

6. Solve your equation in Item 5 to find the greatest percent of discount the store could give without taking a loss. 37.5%.

Look Back

7. Choose another number to check your answer. Was the percent change the same? Possible answer: $20, Increased price $32, Greatest decrease: 37.5%; the answers are the same.

SOLVE ANOTHER PROBLEM

A store has increased its wholesale prices 150%. What is the greatest percent of discount it can offer during a sale without selling its products below cost? 60%.

Name ____________________

Guided Problem Solving 7-1

GPS **PROBLEM 40, STUDENT PAGE 329**

Solve this puzzle: "The number is greater than 500 and less than 550. The number is odd and is a multiple of 9 and the ones digit is 1. What is the number?"

Understand

1. What numbers will the mystery number fall between? 500 and 550
2. The mystery number is a multiple of which number? 9
3. What is the ones digit in the mystery number? 1

Plan

4. Let x = the mystery number. Write an inequality that shows which numbers the mystery number falls between.
   $500 < x < 550$
5. How can you use divisibility rules to determine if a number is a multiple of 9? The sum of the digits is a number that can be divided by 9.

Solve

6. List the numbers with a 1 in the ones place that would solve the inequality you wrote in Item 4.
   501, 511, 521, 531, 541
7. Use divisibility rules to find which of the numbers in Item 6 is divisible by 9. 531

Look Back

8. Why could you ignore the clue that the mystery number is odd? Possible answer: Since the ones digit is 1, it is given that the mystery number is odd.

SOLVE ANOTHER PROBLEM

Solve this puzzle: "The number is less than 475 but greater than 425. The number is a multiple of 3, 6, and 9 and the ones digit is 2. What is the number?" 432

Name ____________________

Guided Problem Solving 7-2

GPS **PROBLEM 36, STUDENT PAGE 334**

Dr. Pascal studies the effects of light sources on house plants. The number of plants in each class are (24, 30, 36, and 42.) He wants to subdivide the classes into groups of the same size for the research project. What is the largest group size that will work in all four classes?

Understand

1. Circle the number of plants in each of the four classes.
2. Are the groups to be the same size or different sizes? Same size.

Plan

3. How can finding the GCF of the class sizes help you find the group size? Possible answer: It gives the greatest number that can be evenly divided into all the class sizes.
4. Make a factor tree for the number of plants in each class. Possible answer:

   24 → (2) 12 → (2) 6 → (2) (3)
   30 → (2) 15 → (3) (5)
   36 → (2) 18 → (2) 9 → (3) (3)
   42 → (2) 21 → (3) (7)

Solve

5. What are the common factors for all four numbers? 2 and 3
6. What is the largest group size for the four classes? 6 plants.

Look Back

7. What is another way to find the GCF of a group of numbers? Possible answer: Make a list of the multiples of each class size.

SOLVE ANOTHER PROBLEM

In another study, the number of plants in each class are 32, 40, 48, and 64. Dr. Pascal wants to subdivide the classes into groups of the same size. What is the largest group size that will work in all four classes? 8 plants.

Name ____________________

Guided Problem Solving 7-3

GPS **PROBLEM 22, STUDENT PAGE 338**

Suppose Earth and Mars were aligned with the sun. Earth completes its orbit in 365 days and Mars completes its orbit in 687 days (orbits rounded to the nearest Earth day). When do both planets return to these same positions in their orbits?

Understand

1. How many days does it take the Earth to complete an orbit? 365 days.
2. How many days does it take Mars to complete an orbit? 687 days.

Plan

3. How can finding the LCM of the days it takes each planet to make one orbit around the sun help you find the number of days until the planets are aligned again? Possible answer: It gives the smallest number of complete orbits for each planet to return to the original positions.
4. Make a factor tree for each number.

   365 → (5) (73)
   687 → (3) (229)

Solve

5. What are the prime factors of 365 and 687? 3, 5, 73, and 229
6. What is the highest power of each prime factor? 3, 5, 73, and 229
7. When will the planets return to these same positions in their orbits?
   250,755 days = 687 years.

Look Back

8. Why should you express your answer in years?
   Possible answer: Because it is easier to understand.

SOLVE ANOTHER PROBLEM

Suppose Earth and Venus were aligned with the sun. Earth completes its orbit in 365 days and Venus its in 225 days (orbits rounded to the nearest Earth day). How many days until the planets are aligned again?
16,425 days = 45 years.

Name ____________________

Guided Problem Solving 7-4

GPS **PROBLEM 23, STUDENT PAGE 348**

Marine animals, like the porpoise and the sea cow, get oxygen by breathing air, not from the water through gills, as fish do. A sea cow can stay underwater for $\frac{9}{30}$ hour. A porpoise can be underwater for $\frac{1}{4}$ hour. Which marine mammal can stay underwater longer?

Understand

1. What are you asked to find? Whether a sea cow or a porpoise stays underwater longer.
2. How long can a sea cow stay underwater? $\frac{9}{30}$ hour.
3. How long can a porpoise stay underwater? $\frac{1}{4}$ hour.

Plan

4. What do you need to do first in order to compare fractions with different denominators? Rewrite the fractions with a common denominator.
5. What do you need to do next? Compare the numerators.
6. What is the LCD of 4 and 30? 60

Solve

7. Rewrite $\frac{9}{30}$ and $\frac{1}{4}$ using the LCD. $\frac{9}{30} = \frac{18}{60}$ $\frac{1}{4} = \frac{15}{60}$
8. Which fraction is larger? $\frac{18}{60} > \frac{15}{60}$
9. Which marine mammal can stay underwater longer? A sea cow.

Look Back

10. How could you find the answer by writing each time as a decimal? Possible answer: Compare the place value of the digits.

SOLVE ANOTHER PROBLEM

Ken practiced shooting basketball free throws for $\frac{1}{3}$ hour. Max practiced shooting free throws for $\frac{2}{5}$ hour. Who practiced shooting longer? Max.

Name ______

Guided Problem Solving 7-5

GPS PROBLEM 29, STUDENT PAGE 354

Ana's stock rose $\frac{3}{4}$ of a point Wednesday, rose $\frac{3}{8}$ of a point Thursday, and fell $1\frac{1}{4}$ points Friday. Write an algebraic expression for the situation and find the overall change in her stock for these three days.

Understand

1. Underline the number of points the stock rose.
2. Circle the number of points the stock fell.
3. What two things are you asked to do? Write an algebraic expression and find the overall change in stock price.

Plan

4. Would a rising stock price be a positive or a negative number? Positive.
5. Would a falling stock price be a positive or a negative number? Negative.

Solve

6. Write an expression for the change in stock price. Possible answer: $\frac{3}{4} + \frac{3}{8} + (-1\frac{1}{4})$
7. Simplify your expression. $\frac{-1}{8}$
8. What is the overall change in stock price. Down $\frac{1}{8}$ of a point.

Look Back

9. How could you have used a calculator to find the answer? Would this be easier? Explain. Possible answer: Change fractions to decimals. Yes, less chance for calculation error.

SOLVE ANOTHER PROBLEM

Joe's stock rose $\frac{5}{8}$ of a point Monday, fell $\frac{7}{8}$ of a point Tuesday, and fell $2\frac{1}{2}$ points Wednesday. Write an algebraic expression for the situation and find the overall change in his stock for these three days.

$(+\frac{5}{8}) + (-\frac{7}{8}) + (-2\frac{1}{2}) = -2\frac{3}{4}$; Down $2\frac{3}{4}$ points.

Name ______

Guided Problem Solving 7-6

GPS PROBLEM 28, STUDENT PAGE 360

Some say that the average ratio of inches of snow to inches of water is 10 to 1. If the snow is equivalent to $2\frac{7}{8}$ inches of water, how many inches of snow are there? Explain your reasoning.

Possible answers: Items 4, 7, 8

Understand

1. What are you asked to find? How many inches of snow are equivalent to $2\frac{7}{8}$ inches of water.
2. What is the average ratio of inches of snow to inches of water? 10 to 1

Plan

3. Write $2\frac{7}{8}$ as a decimal. 2.875
4. Let x represent inches of snow. Write a proportion for the problem using 10 to 1 and x. $\frac{10}{1} = \frac{x}{2.875}$

Solve

5. Solve for x. 28.75
6. How many inches of snow is equivalent to $2\frac{7}{8}$ inches of water? 28.75 in.
7. Explain your reasoning. Proportion shows the relationship between inches of snow and rain. Solving the proportion will give the missing measurement.

Look Back

8. How could you have found the answer using an improper fraction? Convert the mixed number, write the proportions, and simplify.

SOLVE ANOTHER PROBLEM

The average ratio of inches of rain to inches of snow is 1 to 10. How many inches of rain is equivalent to $16\frac{1}{2}$ inches of snow? Explain your reasoning.

1.65 in.; $\frac{1}{10} = \frac{x}{16.5}$; $x = 1.65$; Proportion shows the relationship between inches of rain and snow. Solving the proportion will give the missing measurements.

Name ______

Guided Problem Solving 7-7

GPS PROBLEM 23, STUDENT PAGE 368

The formula $t = \frac{\sqrt{d}}{4}$ shows how to find the time (t), in seconds, that it takes a falling object to free-fall a given distance (d). Find the falling time for a skydiver to fall 900 feet before opening the parachute.

Understand

1. What does the t in the formula $t = \frac{\sqrt{d}}{4}$ stand for? Time in seconds.
2. What does the d in the formula $t = \frac{\sqrt{d}}{4}$ stand for? Distance in feet.
3. You are asked to find how long it takes to fall how many feet? 900 feet.

Plan

4. What is the first step in solving the formula? b
   a. Divide d by 4. b. Find the square root of d.
5. What is the second step in solving the formula? Divide $\sqrt{d}$ by 4.
6. What number will you substitute in the formula? 900 for d.
7. Which is a reasonable time? c
   a. 900 seconds b. 30 seconds c. 8 seconds

Solve

8. Solve using the formula. $t = 7.5$
9. How many seconds does it takes to free-fall 900 feet. 7.5 seconds.

Look Back

10. If your answer and your estimate are not close, how can you determine if your answer is reasonable? Possible answer: Recalculate answer and estimate. Then compare.

SOLVE ANOTHER PROBLEM

Find the falling time for a skydiver to fall 1600 feet before opening the parachute.

10 seconds.

Name ______

Guided Problem Solving 7-8

GPS PROBLEM 28, STUDENT PAGE 372

You can find the number of seconds that it takes a pendulum to swing back and forth. First, find the square root of the pendulum's length in meters, then double it. How long will it take a pendulum that is 1.2 meters long to swing back and forth?

Understand

1. What are you asked to find? The number of seconds it takes a 1.2 meter long pendulum to swing back and forth.
2. What is the pendulum's length? 1.2 meters.
3. Underline the steps to use in finding the number of seconds.

Plan

4. How can you find the square root of a number using a calculator? Enter the number, then press the $\sqrt{x}$ (square root) key.
5. How would you double a number? Multiply by 2.

Solve

6. Use a calculator to find the square root of 1.2. Round the answer to the nearest thousandth. 1.095
7. Double the square root of 1.2. 2.19
8. How long will it take a 1.2 meter pendulum to swing back and forth? ≈ 2.19 seconds.

Look Back

9. Why is it important to follow the steps in order? What happens if you switch the order? Possible answer: If the order changes, the answer is different.

SOLVE ANOTHER PROBLEM

How long will it take a pendulum that is 9.6 meters long to swing back and forth?

≈ 6.196 seconds.

Name

Guided Problem Solving 7-9

GPS PROBLEM 15, STUDENT PAGE 378

A square courtyard with a diagonal walkway has an area of 81 square feet.

a. Find the length of the sides of the courtyard.

b. Find the length of the walkway.

Understand

1. What is the area of the square courtyard? 81 square feet.
2. What figure is formed by two sides of the courtyard and the diagonal walkway? Right triangle.
3. What part of the figure named in Item 2 represents the longest part of the walkway? Hypotenuse.

Plan

4. How can you find the length of each courtyard side? Find $\sqrt{81}$.
5. How can the Pythagorean Theorem help find the walkway length? Let the sides of the square be the legs. Solve for *c*.

Solve

6. What is the length of each side of the courtyard? 9 feet.
7. What is the length of the longest part of the walkway rounded to the nearest thousandth? 12.728 feet.

Look Back

8. How can you check your answer? Possible answer: Substitute answers for variables in the Pythagorean Theorem. $a^2 + b^2 = c^2$, $9^2 + 9^2 = 12.728^2$; $81 + 81 \approx 162$.

SOLVE ANOTHER PROBLEM

A square courtyard with a diagonal walkway has an area of 324 ft². Find the length of

a. the sides of the courtyard. 18 feet. b. the walkway. $\approx$ 25.5 feet.

Name

Guided Problem Solving 8-1

GPS PROBLEM 15, STUDENT PAGE 394

For a geology experiment, a group of students measure the mass of a piece of copper. Their results were 15.64 g, 15.69 g, 15.67 g, 0.01566 kg, and 0.01564 kg. What is the average of the students' measurements?

Understand

1. What are you asked to find? Average of five measurements.
2. Underline the measurements of the copper piece.

Plan

3. How do you find the average of a set of numbers? Find the sum of the numbers and divide by the number of addends.
4. To convert from kilograms to grams, which ratio will you use? a

a. $\frac{1000 \text{ g}}{1 \text{ kg}}$ b. $\frac{1 \text{ kg}}{1000 \text{ g}}$

Solve

5. Convert the measurements from kilograms to grams.

a. 0.01566 kg 15.66 g b. 0.01564 kg 15.64 g

6. What is the sum of the measures in grams? 78.3 g
7. What is the average mass? 15.66 g

Look Back

8. How could you Work Backward to check your answer? Multiply the average mass by 5, then subtract each of the five masses. The result should be zero.

SOLVE ANOTHER PROBLEM

For a math activity, a group of students measured the length of piece of string. Their results were 234.4 cm, 235 cm, 2.34 m, and 2.348 m. What is the average of the students' measurements? 234.55 cm

Name

Guided Problem Solving 8-2

GPS PROBLEM 19, STUDENT PAGE 400

An Olympic marathon covers 42.2 km of distance through the streets of the host city, followed by a 400 m lap around the main stadium. What is the total distance of the race, in meters? Use significant digits.

Understand

1. What are you asked to find? Total distance of race in meters.
2. What is the length of the part of the race through the streets? 42.2 km
3. What is the length of the lap in the stadium? 400 m

Plan

4. How many meters are in a kilometer? 1000 m
5. Convert 42.2 km to meters. 42,200 m
6. Which operation will you use to find the total distance of the marathon? Addition.

Solve

7. Write an equation to find the total distance of the marathon. 42,200 + 400 = 42,600
8. What is the total distance? 42,600 m
9. What are the significant digits in the total distance? 4, 2, 6, 0

Look Back

10. What are two ways to convert 42.2 km to meters? Set up a proportion and solve; move decimal to multiply by a power of ten.

SOLVE ANOTHER PROBLEM

A bicycle race covers 34.8 km over winding country roads and 500 m in the final straight stretch across the finish line. What is the total distance of the race, in meters? 35,300 m

Name

Guided Problem Solving 8-3

GPS PROBLEM 16, STUDENT PAGE 406

The west coast of Cuba is at 85° W and the east coast of Cuba is at 74° W. If at that latitude, a 5° change in longitude represents about 300 mi, how far is it from coast to coast? Explain your answer. Possible answer: Item 9

Understand

1. What is the longitude at the west coast? 85° W
2. What is the longitude at the east coast? 74° W

Plan

4. Given the longitude, which operation will you use to find the distance across Cuba in degrees? Subtraction.
5. How many miles is represented by a 1° change in longitude at that latitude? 60 miles.
6. Which operation will you use to find the distance across Cuba in miles? Multiplication.

Solve

7. How many degrees is it between the west and east coasts of Cuba? 11°
8. What is the distance in miles between the west and east coasts of Cuba? 660 miles.
9. Explain your answer. If 1° is about 60 miles, then 11° is $11 \cdot 60$, or 660 miles.

Look Back

10. Show how you could find the answer by writing and solving a proportion. Let x = miles, $\frac{5}{300} = \frac{11}{x}$; $5x = 11 \cdot 300$, $x = 660$.

SOLVE ANOTHER PROBLEM

Possible explanation:

The west coast of Australia is at 113° E and the east coast of Australia is at 153° E. If at that latitude, a 10° change in longitude represents about 625 mi, how far is it from coast to coast? Explain your answer. 2500 mi; if 1° is about 62.5 miles, then 40° is $(40 \cdot 62.5)$ mi.

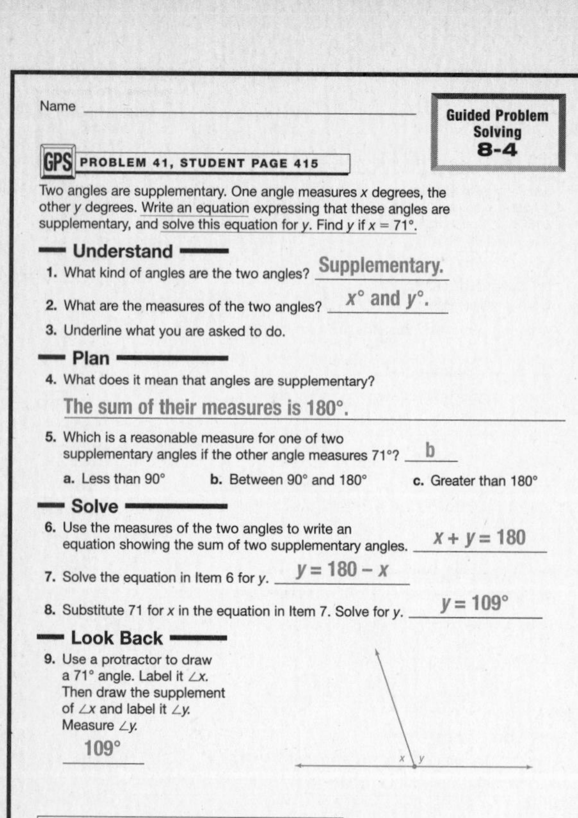
Name ______________________

Guided Problem Solving 8-4

GPS PROBLEM 41, STUDENT PAGE 415

Two angles are supplementary. One angle measures x degrees, the other y degrees. Write an equation expressing that these angles are supplementary, and solve this equation for y. Find y if $x = 71°$.

Understand

1. What kind of angles are the two angles? Supplementary.
2. What are the measures of the two angles? $x°$ and $y°$.
3. Underline what you are asked to do.

Plan

4. What does it mean that angles are supplementary?
The sum of their measures is 180°.
5. Which is a reasonable measure for one of two supplementary angles if the other angle measures 71°? b
a. Less than 90° b. Between 90° and 180° c. Greater than 180°

Solve

6. Use the measures of the two angles to write an equation showing the sum of two supplementary angles. $x + y = 180$
7. Solve the equation in Item 6 for y. $y = 180 - x$
8. Substitute 71 for x in the equation in Item 7. Solve for y. $y = 109°$

Look Back

9. Use a protractor to draw a 71° angle. Label it $\angle x$. Then draw the supplement of $\angle x$ and label it $\angle y$. Measure $\angle y$.
109°

SOLVE ANOTHER PROBLEM

Two angles are complementary. One angle measures x degrees, the other y degrees. Write an equation expressing the fact that these angles are complementary, and solve this equation for y. Find y if $x = 29°$.
$x + y = 90$; $y = 90 - x$; $y = 61°$

Use with page 415. 57

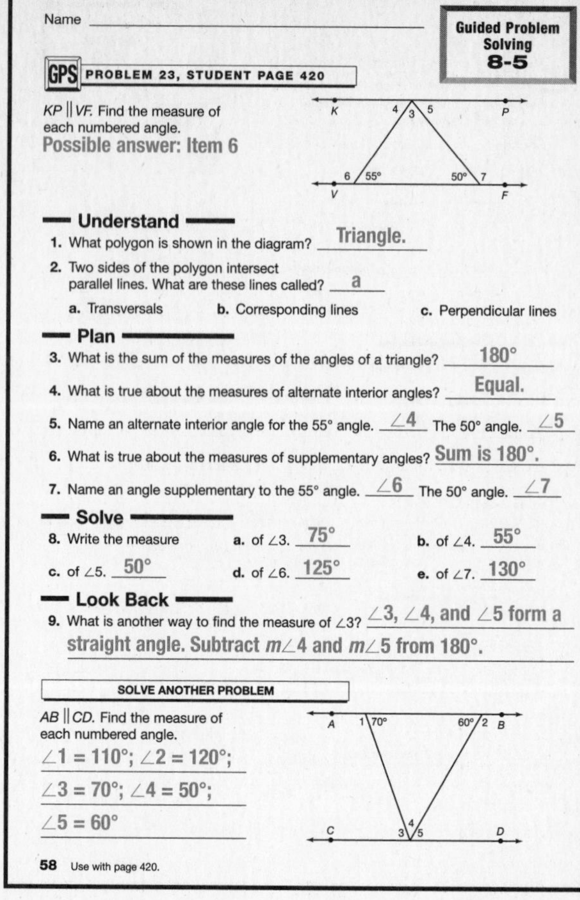
Name ______________________

Guided Problem Solving 8-5

GPS PROBLEM 23, STUDENT PAGE 420

$KP \parallel VF$. Find the measure of each numbered angle.
Possible answer: Item 6

Understand

1. What polygon is shown in the diagram? Triangle.
2. Two sides of the polygon intersect parallel lines. What are these lines called? a
a. Transversals b. Corresponding lines c. Perpendicular lines

Plan

3. What is the sum of the measures of the angles of a triangle? 180°
4. What is true about the measures of alternate interior angles? Equal.
5. Name an alternate interior angle for the 55° angle. $\angle 4$ The 50° angle. $\angle 5$
6. What is true about the measures of supplementary angles? Sum is 180°.
7. Name an angle supplementary to the 55° angle. $\angle 6$ The 50° angle. $\angle 7$

Solve

8. Write the measure a. of $\angle 3$. 75° b. of $\angle 4$. 55°
c. of $\angle 5$. 50° d. of $\angle 6$. 125° e. of $\angle 7$. 130°

Look Back

9. What is another way to find the measure of $\angle 3$? $\angle 3$, $\angle 4$, and $\angle 5$ form a straight angle. Subtract $m\angle 4$ and $m\angle 5$ from 180°.

SOLVE ANOTHER PROBLEM

$AB \parallel CD$. Find the measure of each numbered angle.
$\angle 1 = 110°$; $\angle 2 = 120°$;
$\angle 3 = 70°$; $\angle 4 = 50°$;
$\angle 5 = 60°$

58 Use with page 420.

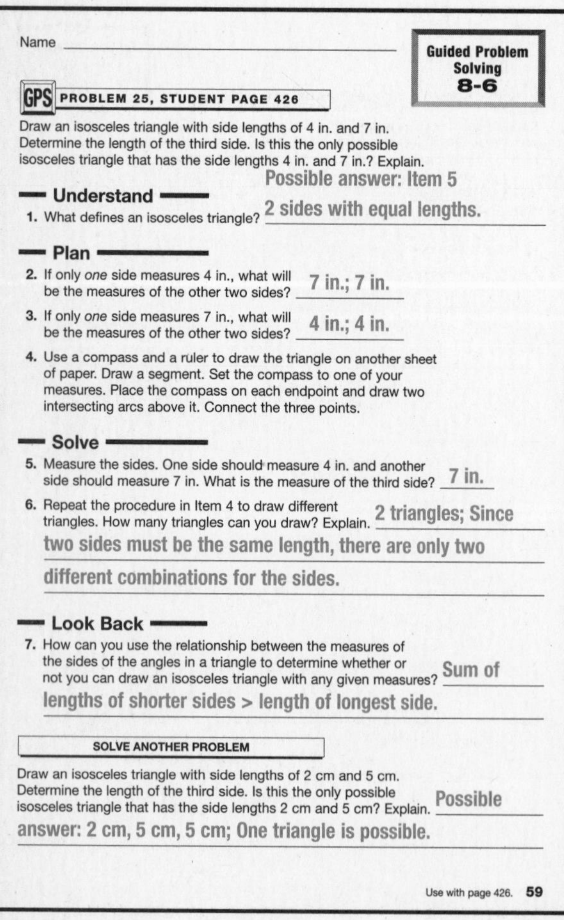
Name ______________________

Guided Problem Solving 8-6

GPS PROBLEM 25, STUDENT PAGE 426

Draw an isosceles triangle with side lengths of 4 in. and 7 in. Determine the length of the third side. Is this the only possible isosceles triangle that has the side lengths 4 in. and 7 in.? Explain.
Possible answer: Item 5

Understand

1. What defines an isosceles triangle? 2 sides with equal lengths.

Plan

2. If only *one* side measures 4 in., what will be the measures of the other two sides? 7 in.; 7 in.
3. If only *one* side measures 7 in., what will be the measures of the other two sides? 4 in.; 4 in.
4. Use a compass and a ruler to draw the triangle on another sheet of paper. Draw a segment. Set the compass to one of your measures. Place the compass on each endpoint and draw two intersecting arcs above it. Connect the three points.

Solve

5. Measure the sides. One side should measure 4 in. and another side should measure 7 in. What is the measure of the third side? 7 in.
6. Repeat the procedure in Item 4 to draw different triangles. How many triangles can you draw? Explain. 2 triangles; Since two sides must be the same length, there are only two different combinations for the sides.

Look Back

7. How can you use the relationship between the measures of the sides of the angles in a triangle to determine whether or not you can draw an isosceles triangle with any given measures? Sum of lengths of shorter sides > length of longest side.

SOLVE ANOTHER PROBLEM

Draw an isosceles triangle with side lengths of 2 cm and 5 cm. Determine the length of the third side. Is this the only possible isosceles triangle that has the side lengths 2 cm and 5 cm? Explain. Possible answer: 2 cm, 5 cm, 5 cm; One triangle is possible.

Use with page 426. 59

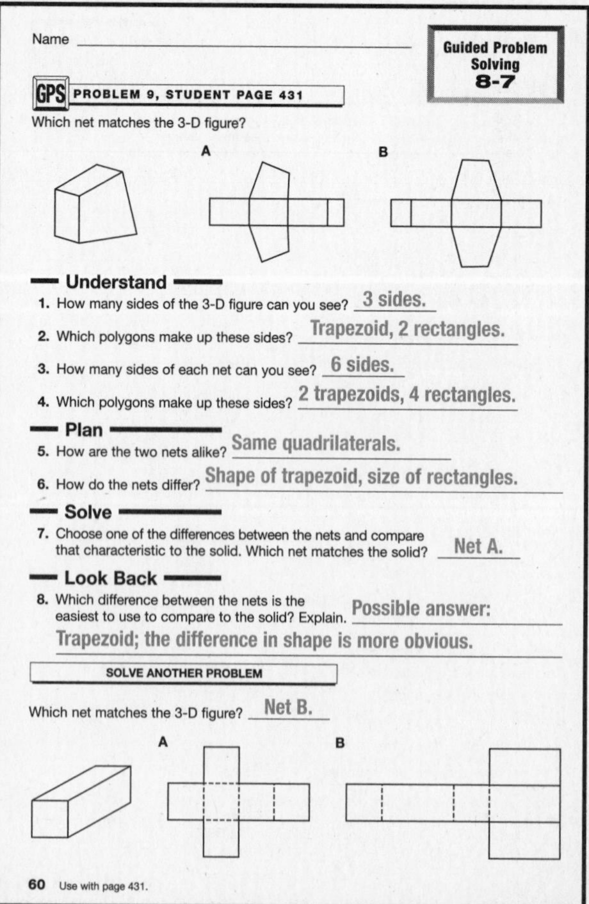
Name ______________________

Guided Problem Solving 8-7

GPS PROBLEM 9, STUDENT PAGE 431

Which net matches the 3-D figure?

Understand

1. How many sides of the 3-D figure can you see? 3 sides.
2. Which polygons make up these sides? Trapezoid, 2 rectangles.
3. How many sides of each net can you see? 6 sides.
4. Which polygons make up these sides? 2 trapezoids, 4 rectangles.

Plan

5. How are the two nets alike? Same quadrilaterals.
6. How do the nets differ? Shape of trapezoid, size of rectangles.

Solve

7. Choose one of the differences between the nets and compare that characteristic to the solid. Which net matches the solid? Net A.

Look Back

8. Which difference between the nets is the easiest to use to compare to the solid? Explain. Possible answer: Trapezoid; the difference in shape is more obvious.

SOLVE ANOTHER PROBLEM

Which net matches the 3-D figure? Net B.

60 Use with page 431.

Name ______________________

Guided Problem Solving 9-1

GPS PROBLEM 15, STUDENT PAGE 448

A set designer wants to make a parlor room 16 ft by 24 ft.

a. How much tape does he need to mark out the room on the stage?

b. How much carpet does he need to cover the whole floor?

Possible answers: Items 5 and 10

Understand

1. What are the dimensions of the parlor room? 16 ft by 24 ft.

2. Will the designer use the tape to mark the perimeter or the area of the room? Perimeter.

3. Will the carpet cover the perimeter or area of the room? Area.

Plan

4. Draw a sketch of the room. Label each measure.

Possible answer:

16 ft

24 ft

5. What is the formula for the perimeter of a rectangle? $P = 2b + 2h.$

6. What is the formula for the area of a rectangle? $A = b \cdot h.$

7. What is a reasonable area for the room? d

a. 80 ft^2 b. 160 ft^2 c. 200 ft^2 d. 400 ft^2

Solve

8. How much tape will be needed to mark out the room on the stage? 80 ft

9. How much carpet will be needed to cover the whole floor? 384 ft^2

Look Back

10. What is another way to find the perimeter? Add lengths of the sides.

SOLVE ANOTHER PROBLEM

An interior designer is designing a room 21 ft by 28 ft.

a. How much wallpaper border does she need to place a strip at the top of the walls around the entire room? 98 ft

b. How much carpet does she need to cover the whole floor? 588 ft^2

Name ______________________

Guided Problem Solving 9-2

GPS PROBLEM 8, STUDENT PAGE 454

A Shakespearean theater group wants to buy material for its new rectangular stage. On the model, the stage is 40 cm by 100 cm. The scale factor reads 25. What is the minimum length of a string of lights around the perimeter of the stage?

Possible answers: Items 4 and 9

Understand

1. What figure is the stage? Rectangle.

2. What are the model's dimensions? 40 cm by 100 cm.

3. What is the scale factor? 25

Plan

4. What is the formula for the perimeter of a rectangle? $P = 2(b + h)$

5. How can you find the dimensions of the stage given the dimensions of the model and the scale factor?

Multiply each dimension by the scale factor.

Solve

6. One dimension of the model is 40 cm. What is this dimension of the actual stage? 1000 cm

7. What is the other dimension of the actual stage? 2500 cm

8. What is the minimum length of a string of lights around the perimeter of the stage? 7000 cm or 70 m

Look Back

9. What is another way to find the length of the lights? Find the perimeter of the model, then multiply it by the scale factor.

$[2 \cdot (40 + 100) \cdot 25 = 7000]$

SOLVE ANOTHER PROBLEM

A model of a stage is 100 cm by 50 cm. The scale factor reads 20. What is the minimum length of raised trim that can be used around the perimeter of the stage? 6000 cm or 60 m

Name ______________________

Guided Problem Solving 9-3

GPS PROBLEM 17, STUDENT PAGE 460

A theater owner wants to design a Greek style semicircular stage with a radius of 30 ft. Explain how to find the perimeter and area of the stage. Include an illustration.

Possible answers: Items 7 and 8

Understand

1. Underline what you are asked to explain.

2. What figure is the stage? Semicircle.

Plan

3. Draw the shape of the stage. Label the radius.

30 ft

4. The area of the stage is what fraction of the area of a circle? $\frac{1}{2}$

5. The curved part of the stage is what fraction of the circumference of a circle? $\frac{1}{2}$

6. How can you find the measure of the straight part? Multiply radius by 2.

Solve

7. Explain how to find the perimeter of the stage. Divide circumference of circle by 2. Add 2 times the radius to the quotient.

8. Explain how to find the area of the stage. Divide area of a circle by 2.

Look Back

9. Follow the steps in your explanations to find the area and perimeter of the stage. Write each measure. Are your explanations complete?

Perimeter = 154.2 ft; Area = 1413 ft^2

SOLVE ANOTHER PROBLEM

Possible answer:

15 ft

A stage has a semicircular section with a radius of 15 ft. A square with sides equal to the straight part of the semicircle extends from that part. Explain how to find the perimeter and area of the stage. Include an illustration.

Perimeter: Divide circumference of circle by 2. Add to 3 times twice the radius. Area: Divide area of circle by 2 and add the quotient to area of the square.

Name ______________________

Guided Problem Solving 9-4

GPS PROBLEM 15, STUDENT PAGE 465

A cereal company is making a jumbo-size box by doubling the dimensions of its midsize box which is 12 in. by 8 in. by 2 in. How much more cardboard will be needed to make the jumbo size?

Understand

1. What are the dimensions of the midsize box? 12 in. × 8 in. × 2 in.

2. How many times greater are the dimensions of the jumbo-size box than the midsize box? Two times.

Plan

3. What are the dimensions of the jumbo-size box? 24 in. × 16 in. × 4 in.

4. How do you find the surface area of the box? Add areas of the faces.

5. Draw and label a net for each box size. Possible answer:

12 8 2 24 16 4

Solve

6. How much cardboard is needed to make the midsize box? 272 in^2

7. How much cardboard is needed to make the jumbo-size box? 1088 in^2

8. How many more square inches of cardboard is needed to make the jumbo-size box than to make the midsize box? 816 in^2

Look Back

9. How does the relationship between the dimensions and surface areas of the two boxes compare to the relationship between the dimensions and area of a dilated rectangle with a scale factor of 2? Possible answer: Dimensions multiplied by 2, SA by 2^2; It is the same.

SOLVE ANOTHER PROBLEM

A company is making a regular-size cracker box by tripling the dimensions of its sample box which is 4 in. by 3 in. by 1 in. How much more cardboard will be needed to make the regular size? 304 in^2

Name ______

Guided Problem Solving 9-5

GPS PROBLEM 9, STUDENT PAGE 471

Sioux tepees are cone-shaped. If the diameter of a tepee is 18 ft and the height is 12 ft, how much buffalo hide is needed to cover the outside surface?

Understand

1. Underline the diameter and height of the tepee.
2. What shape is the tepee? Cone-shaped.
3. Is the floor area inside the tepee covered with buffalo hide? No.

Plan

4. What is the radius of the tepee? 9 ft
5. Which formula you will use to find the area of the curved surface? a

   a. $A = \frac{1}{2}Cs$ b. $A = \pi r^2$ c. $A = Csr^2$
6. What kind of triangle is formed by the slant height, radius, and height of a cone? Right triangle.
7. Which theorem can you use to find the measure of the slant height? Pythagorean Theorem.

Solve

8. What is the slant height of the cone? 15 ft
9. Write an equation to show how to find how much buffalo hide is needed.

   $A = \frac{1}{2} \cdot (\pi \cdot 18) \cdot 15$
10. How much buffalo hide is needed to cover the outside surface? 423.9 ft^2

Look Back

11. Why isn't the area of the opening subtracted to find the amount of buffalo skin needed? Possible answer: Buffalo skin makes up the flap used to cover the opening.

SOLVE ANOTHER PROBLEM

A campsite has platform shelters shaped like cones. If the height of each shelter is 12 feet and the diameter is 10 ft, how much canvas is needed to cover the outside of each shelter 204.1 ft^2

Name ______

Guided Problem Solving 9-6

GPS PROBLEM 9, STUDENT PAGE 479

Sketch the figure. Then find the volume of a fly-casting pool in the park that is 30 ft wide, 40 ft long, and 5 ft deep.

Understand

1. What are you asked to find? Volume of fly-casting pool.
2. What figure is the pond? Rectangular prism.
3. What is each dimension of the pool?

   a. Width 30 ft   b. Length 40 ft   c. Depth 5 ft

Plan

4. Sketch the figure for the pond. Label each dimension.

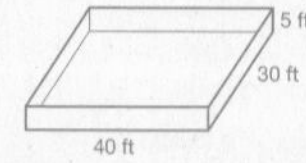

5. How can you find the volume of the pond? Possible answer: Multiply the area of the base (B) by the height (h).
6. How can you find the area of the bottom of the pool? Possible answer: Multiply length and width.

Solve

7. What is the area of the bottom of the pool? 1200 ft^2
8. What is the volume of the pool? 6000 ft^3

Look Back

9. How could you find the volume without drawing a sketch? Possible answer: Substitute values in the formula: $A = B \cdot h$.

SOLVE ANOTHER PROBLEM

Sketch the figure. Then find the volume of a fish pond at the zoo that is 20 ft wide, 25 ft long, and 3 ft deep.

1500 ft^3

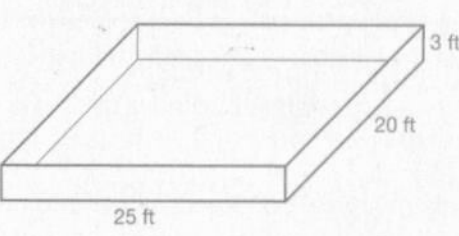

Name ______

Guided Problem Solving 9-7

GPS PROBLEM 13, STUDENT PAGE 486

You have a package 24 in. by 18 in. by 12 in. to ship. E-Z Shipping charges by volume $0.002 per in^3 whereas Speedy Shipping charges by surface area $0.005 per in^2.

a. Which company is cheaper for this package?

b. Will this be true for all shapes of packages? Explain.

Understand

Possible answers: Items 10 and 11

1. Underline the dimensions of the package.
2. Circle each company's rate.

Plan

3. What formula can you use to find the volume of the package? $V = B \cdot h$
4. Sketch the net for the package.

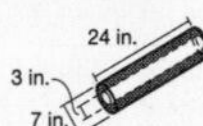

5. What formula can you use to find the area of each face? $A = b \cdot h$
6. Which operation will you use to find the cost? Multiplication.

Solve

7. Find the volume of the package. 5184 in^3 The surface area. 1872 in^2
8. What is the shipping cost for each company?

   a. E-Z Shipping $10.37   b. Speedy Shipping $9.36
9. Which company is cheaper for this package? Speedy Shipping.
10. Will this be true for all shapes of packages? Explain. No, volume and surface area do not have a linear relationship.

Look Back

11. Would calculations be easier if rates and measurements were converted to feet before multiplying? Explain. Yes, smaller numbers may result in less chance for errors.

SOLVE ANOTHER PROBLEM

Use the rates above. Is it cheaper to ship a package measuring 12 in. by 20 in. by 4 in. using E-Z Shipping or Speedy Shipping? E-Z Shipping ($1.92 vs $3.68 for Speedy)

Name ______

Guided Problem Solving 9-8

GPS PROBLEM 11, STUDENT PAGE 491

Find the volume of the shaded region in the figure.

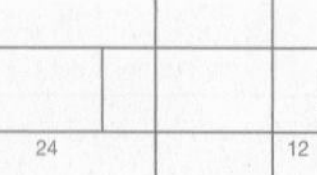

Understand

Possible answers: Items 7 and 11

1. Which two solids make up the figure? Cylinders.
2. What is the diameter of the inside figure? 3 in. The outside figure? 7 in.
3. What is the height of both figures? 24 in.

Plan

4. What is the radius of the inside figure? 1.5 in. The outside figure? 3.5 in.
5. What is the formula for finding the volume of a cylinder? $V = B \cdot h$
6. What is the formula for finding the area of the flat part of a cylinder?

   $A = \pi r^2$
7. How can you find the volume of the shaded region? Subtract volume of inside cylinder from volume of outside cylinder.

Solve

8. What is the volume of the outside cylinder? 923.16 in^3
9. What is the volume of the inside cylinder? 169.56 in^3
10. What is the volume of the shaded region? 753.6 in^3

Look Back

11. What is another way to find the volume of the shaded space? Find area of shaded part of the base. Multiply by cylinder's height.

SOLVE ANOTHER PROBLEM

Find the volume of the shaded region in the figure.

2009.6 in^3

12 in. 4 in. 20 in.

Name ______________________

Guided Problem Solving 9-9

GPS PROBLEM 13, STUDENT PAGE 496

Which solid has a greater volume, the pyramid or cone?

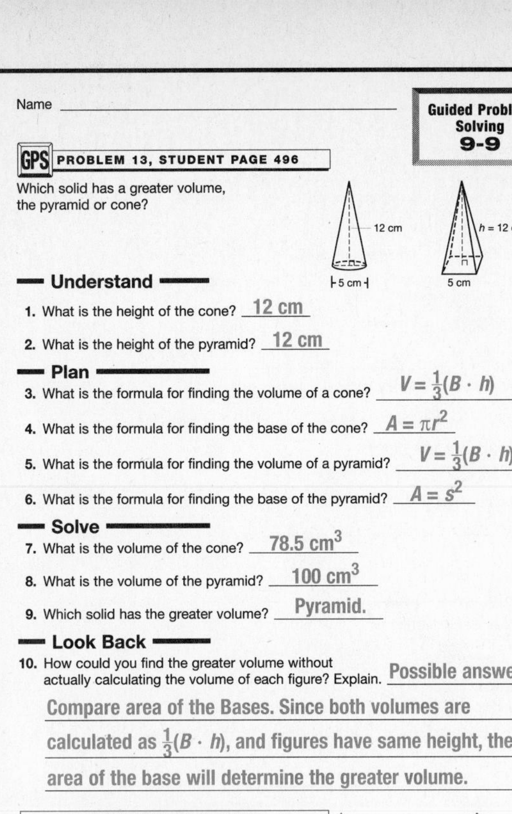

Understand

1. What is the height of the cone? 12 cm
2. What is the height of the pyramid? 12 cm

Plan

3. What is the formula for finding the volume of a cone? $V = \frac{1}{3}(B \cdot h)$
4. What is the formula for finding the base of the cone? $A = \pi r^2$
5. What is the formula for finding the volume of a pyramid? $V = \frac{1}{3}(B \cdot h)$
6. What is the formula for finding the base of the pyramid? $A = s^2$

Solve

7. What is the volume of the cone? 78.5 cm^3
8. What is the volume of the pyramid? 100 cm^3
9. Which solid has the greater volume? Pyramid.

Look Back

10. How could you find the greater volume without actually calculating the volume of each figure? Explain. Possible answer: Compare area of the Bases. Since both volumes are calculated as $\frac{1}{3}(B \cdot h)$, and figures have same height, the area of the base will determine the greater volume.

SOLVE ANOTHER PROBLEM

Which solid has a greater volume, the pyramid or cone?

10 in.   5 in.   h = 10 in.   10 in.

Pyramid.

Name ______________________

Guided Problem Solving 10-1

GPS PROBLEM 20, STUDENT PAGE 512

Guess my rule.

If you say...	3	5	6	10
I say...	8	24	35	99

Understand

1. What are the input values? 3, 5, 6, 10
2. What are the output values? 8, 24, 35, 99
3. Is the relationship a function? Yes.

Plan

4. Can one of the following operations and a constant (the same number) be applied to each input value in the table to get each output value?

   a. Addition? No.   b. Subtraction? No.   c. Multiplication? No.

   d. Division? No.   e. Exponents (x^2, x^3...) No.

5. Which operation and constant when applied to the input value results in a number that is closest to the output value? x^2
6. What do you need to do to your anwer to Item 5 to obtain the output value? b

   a. Add 1.   b. Subtract 1.   c. Add 2.

Solve

7. What is the rule? Square the input value, then subtract 1.

Look Back

8. How can you tell that you will need to multiply or use an exponent in the function? Output value increases by a greater factor than the input value.

SOLVE ANOTHER PROBLEM

Guess my rule.

If you say...	2	3	4	8
I say...	6	11	18	66

Square the input value, then add 2.

Name ______________________

Guided Problem Solving 10-2

GPS PROBLEM 11, STUDENT PAGE 516

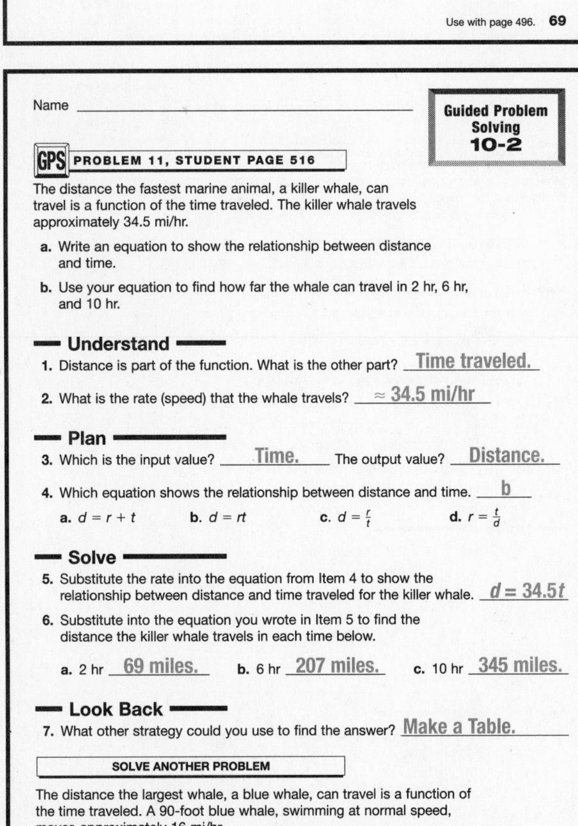

The distance the fastest marine animal, a killer whale, can travel is a function of the time traveled. The killer whale travels approximately 34.5 mi/hr.

a. Write an equation to show the relationship between distance and time.

b. Use your equation to find how far the whale can travel in 2 hr, 6 hr, and 10 hr.

Understand

1. Distance is part of the function. What is the other part? Time traveled.
2. What is the rate (speed) that the whale travels? ≈ 34.5 mi/hr

Plan

3. Which is the input value? Time. The output value? Distance.
4. Which equation shows the relationship between distance and time. b

   a. $d = r + t$ b. $d = rt$ c. $d = \frac{r}{t}$ d. $r = \frac{t}{d}$

Solve

5. Substitute the rate into the equation from Item 4 to show the relationship between distance and time traveled for the killer whale. $d = 34.5t$
6. Substitute into the equation you wrote in Item 5 to find the distance the killer whale travels in each time below.

   a. 2 hr 69 miles.   b. 6 hr 207 miles.   c. 10 hr 345 miles.

Look Back

7. What other strategy could you use to find the answer? Make a Table.

SOLVE ANOTHER PROBLEM

The distance the largest whale, a blue whale, can travel is a function of the time traveled. A 90-foot blue whale, swimming at normal speed, moves approximately 16 mi/hr.

a. Write an equation to show the relationship between distance and time. $d = 16t$

b. Use your equation to find how far the whale can travel for each time.

2 hr 32 miles.   5 hr 80 miles.   8 hr 128 miles.

Name ______________________

Guided Problem Solving 10-3

GPS PROBLEM 14, STUDENT PAGE 522

A toy rocket was launched into the air. The function $h = 50t - 5t^2$ models this situation, where h = height in m and t = time in sec.

h: 140, 105, 70, 35, 0; t: 0, 2, 4, 6, 8, 10; Time (sec.)

a. When is the rocket 105 m in the air? Explain.

b. What happens at 10 sec?

Understand

1. Circle the function.
2. Which axis in the graph represents height? y-axis.

Plan

3. Can there be more than one time for each height? Why? Yes, different input values can have same output value.
4. How can you find the values? Use the graph.

Solve

5. When is the rocket 105 m in the air? What is happening at this time? At 3 sec and 7 sec; Rocket is rising and coming back to Earth.
6. What is the height at 10 sec? What is happening to the rocket? 0 m; The rocket has come back to earth.

Look Back

7. Why doesn't the graph extend below the x-axis? Rocket does not penetrate the earth. It will not go lower than the launch point.

SOLVE ANOTHER PROBLEM

An object is launched into the air. The function $h = 80t - 16t^2$ models this situation, where h = height in ft and t = time in sec.

h: 100, 80, 60, 40, 20, 0; t: 0, 2, 4, 6; Time (sec.)

a. When is the object 64 feet in the air? Explain. At 1 sec and 4 sec; The object is rising and coming down.

b. What happens at $2\frac{1}{2}$ sec? The object is at its highest point.

Name ______________________

Guided Problem Solving 10-4

GPS PROBLEM 11, STUDENT PAGE 526

Ready Rent-All rental charges for a VCR are as follows.

Rental Time	Rental Fee
One day or portion thereof	\$10.00
over 1 day, up to 3 days	\$20.00
over 3 days, up to 5 days	\$35.00

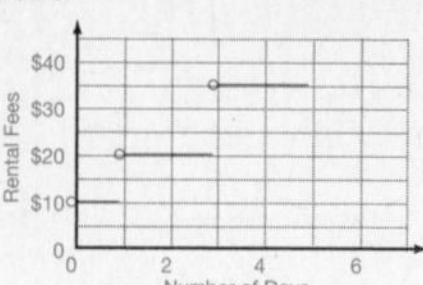

a. Graph the function.

b. What kind of function is this?

Understand

1. What is the fee for renting a VCR for each time period?

a. 0 hr \$0 **b.** 5 hr \$10 **c.** 23 hr \$10 **d.** 25 hr \$20

Plan

2. Which is the independent variable, time or rental fee? Time.

3. On which axis will you graph the number of days? Horizontal, or x-axis.

Solve

4. Graph the function on the grid above.

5. What kind of function did you graph? a

a. Step function **b.** Exponential function **c.** Not a function

Look Back

6. How do you know what kind of function the charges are without graphing? Possible answer: Each fee covers a range of times, so it will be step function.

SOLVE ANOTHER PROBLEM

The video rental store rents game systems as follows.

Rental Time	Rental Fee
One day or portion thereof	\$ 8.00
over 1 day up to 2 days	\$12.00
over 2 days up to 4 days	\$20.00

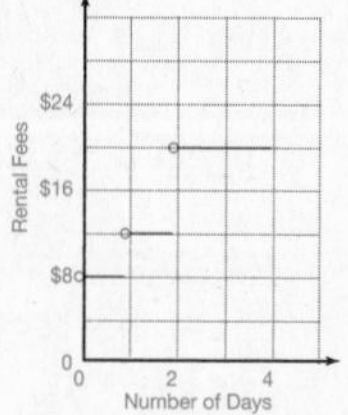

a. Graph the function.

b. What kind of function is this? Step function.

Name ______________________

Guided Problem Solving 10-5

GPS PROBLEM 23, STUDENT PAGE 536

At Epcot Center in Orlando, Florida, the Spaceship Earth is built in the shape of a sphere with a diameter of approximately 165 ft. Use $\pi = 3.14$ to answer each question.

a. Use the formula $S = 4\pi r^2$, where S = surface area and r = radius to find the approximate surface area.

b. Using the formula $V = \frac{4}{3}\pi r^3$, where V = volume and r = radius, find the approximate volume.

Understand

1. What is the diameter? $\approx$ 165 ft

2. Underline the value of π that you will use.

3. Write the formula for surface area. $S = 4\pi r^2$ For volume. $V = \frac{4}{3}\pi r^3$

Plan

4. What is the radius of the sphere? $\approx$ 82.5 ft

5. Find the value of r^2. $\approx$ 6806.25 ft^2 Of r^3. $\approx$ 561,515.625 ft^3

6. Complete the equation to find the surface area. S = $4 \cdot 3.14 \cdot 6806.25$

7. Complete the equation to find the volume. V = $\frac{4}{3} \cdot 3.14 \cdot 561{,}515.625$

Solve

8. Solve each equation.

a. Surface area 85,486.5 ft^2 **b.** Volume 2,350,878.75 ft^3

Look Back

9. Why did you find r^2 and r^3 as the first step in solving both formulas? Possible answer: To follow order of operations.

SOLVE ANOTHER PROBLEM

A museum has an exhibit within a sphere with a diameter of approximately 40 feet. Use $\pi = 3.14$ to answer each question.

a. Use the formula $S = 4\pi r^2$, where S = surface area and r = radius to find the approximate surface area. 5024 ft^2

b. Using the formula $V = \frac{4}{3}\pi r^3$, where V = volume and r = radius, find the approximate volume. $33{,}493.\bar{3}$ ft^3

Name ______________________

Guided Problem Solving 10-6

GPS PROBLEM 27, STUDENT PAGE 541

When asked to simplify $x^2 + x^2$, four students got the following answers. Who is correct? What do you think each of the students did to get their answer?

a. Willard's answer is x^4. **b.** Bryant's answer is $2x^4$.

c. Katie's answer is $2x^2$. **d.** Matt's answer is x^2.

Possible answers: Items 5, 6, and 8

Understand

1. What polynomial are you asked to simplify? $x^2 + x^2$

2. What are you asked to find? Which student added correctly.

Plan

3. How do you add like terms? b

a. Add exponents. **b.** Add coefficients (numbers multiplying each variable).

Solve

4. Which student has the correct answer? Katie.

5. How did Willard find his answer? Added exponents.

6. How did Bryant find his answer? Added exponents and coefficients.

7. How did Katie find her answer? Added coefficients.

8. How did Matt find his answer? Chose one term.

Look Back

9. Write each term as $1x^2$. Then use the distributive property to find the sum. $1x^2 + 1x^2 = x^2(1 + 1) = 2x^2$

SOLVE ANOTHER PROBLEM

Possible answers: Items a and c

When asked to simplify $4x^3 + x^3$, three students got the following answers. Who is correct? Write how you think each student got their answer. Correct answer: Lizzie

a. Su-mi's answer is $4x^6$. Added exponents.

b. Lizzie's answer is $5x^3$. Added coefficients.

c. Mato's answer is $5x^6$. Added exponents and coefficients.

Name ______________________

Guided Problem Solving 10-7

GPS PROBLEM 25, STUDENT PAGE 547

How much higher does a disc propelled upwards with an initial velocity of 40 m/sec go, over time, than one propelled at 30 m/sec from a platform 8 m high? Subtract $-5t^2 + 30t + 8$ from $-5t^2 + 40t$.

Understand

1. Underline the two polynomials you will use when you subtract.

Plan

2. Order the steps below to show how to subtract polynomials.

4 Combine like terms

1 Add the opposite of the second polynomial

3 Group like terms.

2 Find the opposite of all terms in the parentheses.

3. Write the polynomials you will subtract as an expression.

$(-5t^2 + 40t) - (-5t^2 + 30t + 8)$

Solve

4. Use the steps in Item 2 to subtract the polynomial in Item 3.

a. Step 1: $(-5t^2 + 40t) + -(-5t^2 + 30t + 8)$

b. Step 2: $(-5t^2 + 40t) + (5t^2 - 30t - 8)$

c. Step 3: $(-5 + 5)t^2 + (40 - 30)t - 8$

d. Step 4: $10t - 8$

Look Back

5. Show how to write the problem vertically. Then solve to check your answer.

$$\begin{array}{r} -5t^2 + 40t \\ -(-5t^2 + 30t + 8) \\ \hline 10t - 8 \end{array}$$

SOLVE ANOTHER PROBLEM

How much higher does a rocket propelled upwards with an initial velocity of 36 m/sec go, over time, than one propelled at 25 m/sec from a platform 10 m high? Subtract $-5t^2 + 25t + 10$ from $-5t^2 + 36t$. $11t - 10$

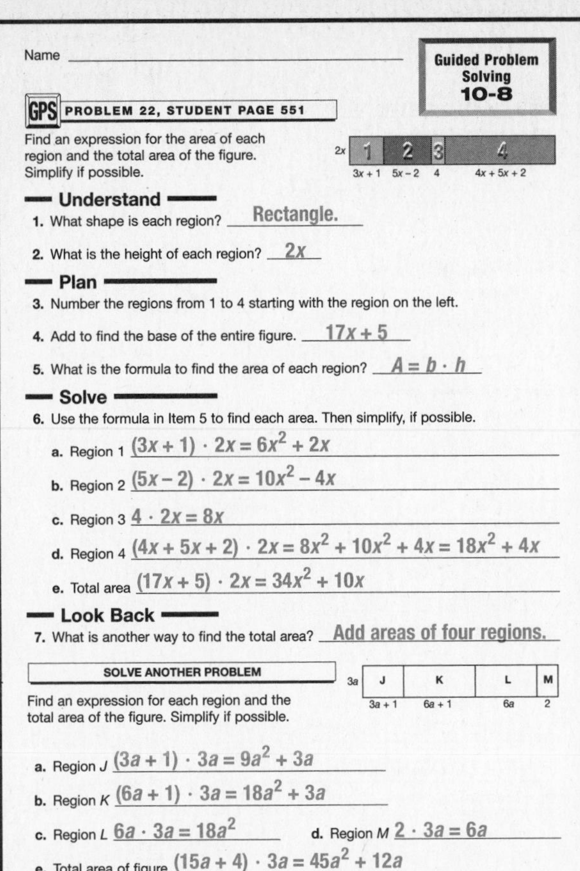
Name ______

Guided Problem Solving 10-8

GPS PROBLEM 22, STUDENT PAGE 551

Find an expression for the area of each region and the total area of the figure. Simplify if possible.

2x | 1 | 2 | 3 | 4 — $3x+1$, $5x-2$, 4, $4x+5x+2$

Understand

1. What shape is each region? Rectangle.
2. What is the height of each region? $2x$

Plan

3. Number the regions from 1 to 4 starting with the region on the left.
4. Add to find the base of the entire figure. $17x+5$
5. What is the formula to find the area of each region? $A = b \cdot h$

Solve

6. Use the formula in Item 5 to find each area. Then simplify, if possible.
   a. Region 1 $(3x+1) \cdot 2x = 6x^2 + 2x$
   b. Region 2 $(5x-2) \cdot 2x = 10x^2 - 4x$
   c. Region 3 $4 \cdot 2x = 8x$
   d. Region 4 $(4x+5x+2) \cdot 2x = 8x^2 + 10x^2 + 4x = 18x^2 + 4x$
   e. Total area $(17x+5) \cdot 2x = 34x^2 + 10x$

Look Back

7. What is another way to find the total area? Add areas of four regions.

SOLVE ANOTHER PROBLEM

3a | J | K | L | M — $3a+1$, $6a+1$, $6a$, 2

Find an expression for each region and the total area of the figure. Simplify if possible.

a. Region J $(3a+1) \cdot 3a = 9a^2 + 3a$
b. Region K $(6a+1) \cdot 3a = 18a^2 + 3a$
c. Region L $6a \cdot 3a = 18a^2$
d. Region M $2 \cdot 3a = 6a$
e. Total area of figure $(15a+4) \cdot 3a = 45a^2 + 12a$

Use with page 551. 77

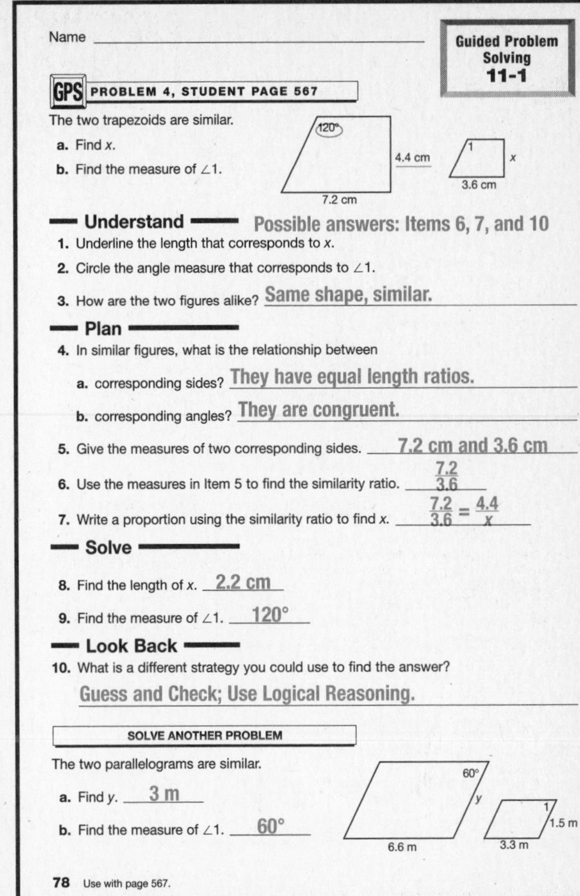
Name ______

Guided Problem Solving 11-1

GPS PROBLEM 4, STUDENT PAGE 567

The two trapezoids are similar.

a. Find x.
b. Find the measure of $\angle 1$.

Understand Possible answers: Items 6, 7, and 10

1. Underline the length that corresponds to x.
2. Circle the angle measure that corresponds to $\angle 1$.
3. How are the two figures alike? Same shape, similar.

Plan

4. In similar figures, what is the relationship between
   a. corresponding sides? They have equal length ratios.
   b. corresponding angles? They are congruent.
5. Give the measures of two corresponding sides. 7.2 cm and 3.6 cm
6. Use the measures in Item 5 to find the similarity ratio. $\frac{7.2}{3.6}$
7. Write a proportion using the similarity ratio to find x. $\frac{7.2}{3.6} = \frac{4.4}{x}$

Solve

8. Find the length of x. 2.2 cm
9. Find the measure of $\angle 1$. 120°

Look Back

10. What is a different strategy you could use to find the answer?
    Guess and Check; Use Logical Reasoning.

SOLVE ANOTHER PROBLEM

The two parallelograms are similar.

a. Find y. 3 m
b. Find the measure of $\angle 1$. 60°

78 Use with page 567.

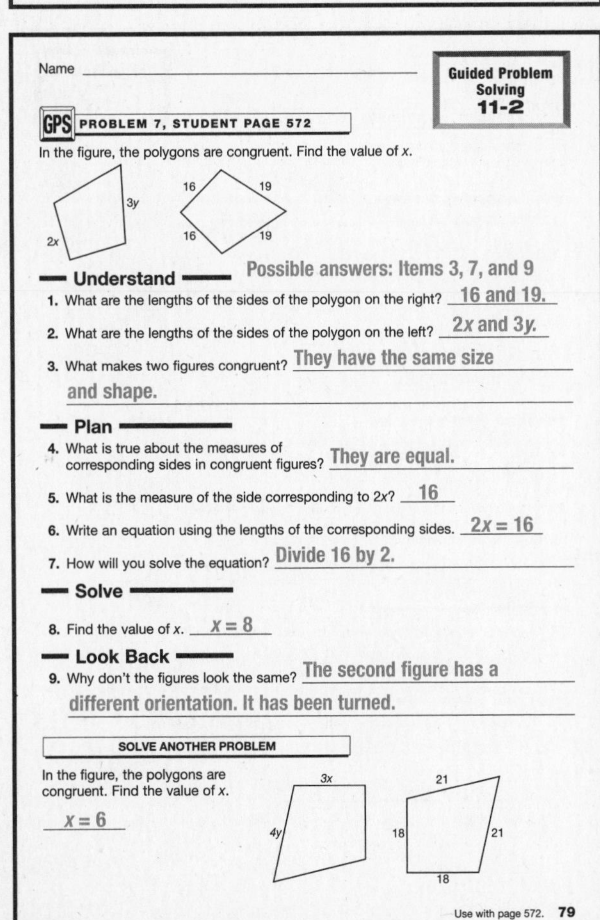
Name ______

Guided Problem Solving 11-2

GPS PROBLEM 7, STUDENT PAGE 572

In the figure, the polygons are congruent. Find the value of x.

Understand Possible answers: Items 3, 7, and 9

1. What are the lengths of the sides of the polygon on the right? 16 and 19.
2. What are the lengths of the sides of the polygon on the left? $2x$ and $3y$.
3. What makes two figures congruent? They have the same size and shape.

Plan

4. What is true about the measures of corresponding sides in congruent figures? They are equal.
5. What is the measure of the side corresponding to $2x$? 16
6. Write an equation using the lengths of the corresponding sides. $2x = 16$
7. How will you solve the equation? Divide 16 by 2.

Solve

8. Find the value of x. $x = 8$

Look Back

9. Why don't the figures look the same? The second figure has a different orientation. It has been turned.

SOLVE ANOTHER PROBLEM

In the figure, the polygons are congruent. Find the value of x.

$x = 6$

Use with page 572. 79

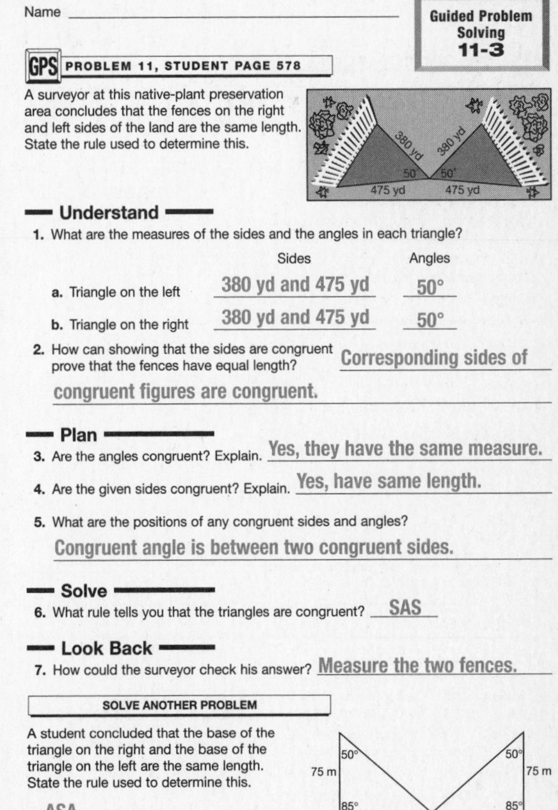
Name ______

Guided Problem Solving 11-3

GPS PROBLEM 11, STUDENT PAGE 578

A surveyor at this native-plant preservation area concludes that the fences on the right and left sides of the land are the same length. State the rule used to determine this.

Understand

1. What are the measures of the sides and the angles in each triangle?

	Sides	Angles
a. Triangle on the left	380 yd and 475 yd	50°
b. Triangle on the right	380 yd and 475 yd	50°

2. How can showing that the sides are congruent prove that the fences have equal length? Corresponding sides of congruent figures are congruent.

Plan

3. Are the angles congruent? Explain. Yes, they have the same measure.
4. Are the given sides congruent? Explain. Yes, have same length.
5. What are the positions of any congruent sides and angles? Congruent angle is between two congruent sides.

Solve

6. What rule tells you that the triangles are congruent? SAS

Look Back

7. How could the surveyor check his answer? Measure the two fences.

SOLVE ANOTHER PROBLEM

A student concluded that the base of the triangle on the right and the base of the triangle on the left are the same length. State the rule used to determine this.

ASA.

80 Use with page 578.

Name ________________________________

Guided Problem Solving 11-4

GPS PROBLEM 10, STUDENT PAGE 583

A model rocket travels straight up from its launch pad. At a point, there is a 55° angle. Determine the distance between the nose of the rocket and the launch pad.

Understand

1. What kind of triangle is formed by the point, the nose of the rocket, and the launch pad? Right triangle.

2. What is the distance from the launch pad to the point? 100 ft

Plan

3. Is the side showing the distance the rocket travels opposite or adjacent to the 55° angle? Opposite.

4. Which ratio will you use to find the distance traveled? c

a. $\sin 55° = \frac{\text{opposite}}{\text{hypotenuse}}$ **b.** $\cos 55° = \frac{\text{adjacent}}{\text{hypotenuse}}$ **c.** $\tan 55° = \frac{\text{opposite}}{\text{adjacent}}$

5. Use your calculator or a table to find the decimal value to the nearest thousandth of the ratio you chose in Item 4. 1.428

Solve

6. Substitute known values in the equation you chose in Item 4. $1.428 = \frac{h}{100}$

7. Solve your equation. What is the distance between the nose of the rocket and the launch pad? 142.8 ft

Look Back

8. How could you use another ratio to find the distance between the nose of the rocket and the launch pad? Subtract the sum of 90° and 55° from 180° to find the measure of the other acute angle. Then use tan 35° to solve.

SOLVE ANOTHER PROBLEM

A model rocket travels straight up from its launch pad. At a point, there is a 50° angle. Determine the distance between the nose of the rocket and the launch pad.

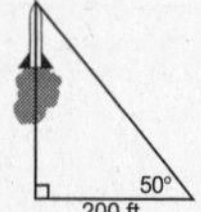

238.4 ft

Name ________________________________

Guided Problem Solving 11-5

GPS PROBLEM 5, STUDENT PAGE 588

On the two triangles shown, $\triangle CBD \sim \triangle CAE$. If $\overline{CD}$ measures 5 cm, what does $\overline{CE}$ measure?

(A) 7.6 cm (B) 7.3 cm
(C) 7.1 cm (D) 7.9 cm

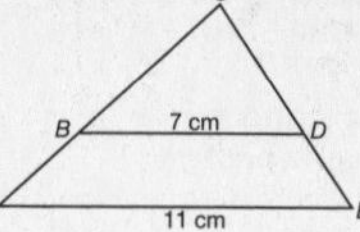

Understand

1. What does the symbol ~ mean? Is similar to.

2. What is the length of *CD*? 5 cm

3. What are you asked to find? Length of $\overline{CE}$.

Plan

4. Identify the corresponding side to each side below.

a. $\overline{AE}$ $\overline{BD}$ **b.** $\overline{CE}$ $\overline{CD}$

5. Write a ratio for the corresponding sides. $\frac{11}{7}$

6. Set up a proportion using the given values for the lengths of the sides. Let *x* represent the unknown side. $\frac{x}{5} = \frac{11}{7}$

Solve

7. Solve the proportion. $x = 7.857$

8. Which answer choice is the correct one? Choice D.

Look Back

9. Why aren't the correct answer choice and your answer to Item 7 the same?
Answer choice is rounded to the nearest tenth.

SOLVE ANOTHER PROBLEM

On the two triangles shown, $\triangle ABC \sim \triangle ADE$. If *AC* measures 4 m, what does *AE* measure?

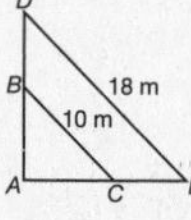

7.2 m

Name ________________________________

Guided Problem Solving 11-6

GPS PROBLEM 9, STUDENT PAGE 599

What transformation, if any, will turn this shape into a math word you've recently learned? (Turning the page and using a mirror may help you decide.)

ROTATE

Understand

1. What will the collection of shapes make when transformed? Math word.

2. Is it possible that the shapes cannot be transformed? Yes.

3. Is it possible that more than one transformation can show the same result? Yes.

Plan

4. If you translate the shape, will a slide help you read the word? No.

5. If you reflect the shape by using a mirror, can you read the word? Yes.

6. If you rotate the shape 180°, can you read the word? No.

Solve

7. What word do the shapes make when transformed? ROTATE.

8. What is the transformation(s)? Reflection.

Look Back

9. How could sketching a coordinate grid around the shapes help you find the word? Possible answer: Plot a reflection and a rotation. Then read the word and describe the transformation.

SOLVE ANOTHER PROBLEM

What transformation, if any, will turn this shape into a math word you've recently learned? (Turning the page and using a mirror may help you decide.)

CONGRUENT

Rotate shapes to read CONGRUENT.

Name ________________________________

Guided Problem Solving 11-7

GPS PROBLEM 14, STUDENT PAGE 604

Reflect the figure across the *y*-axis and give the new coordinates.

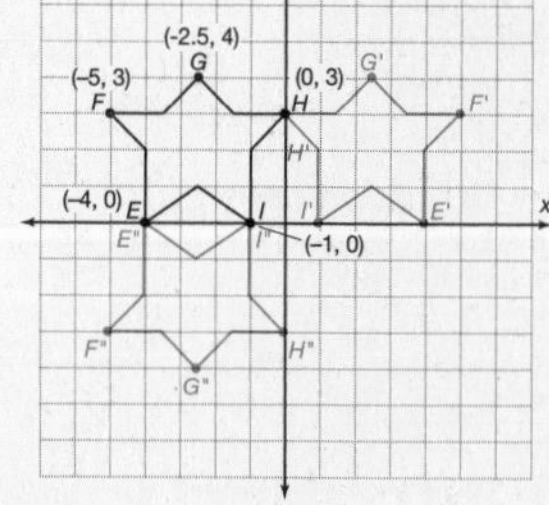

Understand

1. What shape is the figure?
Star.

2. Across which axis will you reflect the figure?
y-axis.

3. What else are you asked for?
New coordinates.

Plan

4. Name the coordinates of the figure above.

E (–4, 0) *F* (–5, 3) *G* (–2.5, 4) *H* (0, 3) *I* (–1, 0)

5. Will the distance from the *y*-axis change or stay the same? Stay same.

6. How will the coordinates change when reflected across the *y*-axis? Signs of *x*-coordinates change, *y*-coordinates stay the same.

Solve

7. Graph the reflection. What are the new coordinates?

E' (4, 0) *F'* (5, 3) *G'* (2.5, 4) *H'* (0, 3) *I'* (1, 0)

Look Back

8. Why does one point not change when the figure is reflected?
The point (0, 3) is on the *y*-axis.

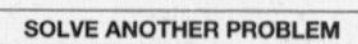

SOLVE ANOTHER PROBLEM

Reflect the figure in the grid above across the *x*-axis and give the new coordinates.

E" (–4, 0) *F"* (–5, –3) *G"* (–2.5, –4) *H"* (0, –3) *I"* (–1, 0)

Name ______

Guided Problem Solving 11-8

GPS **PROBLEM 4, STUDENT PAGE 608**

How many degrees does it take for a regular octagon to rotate onto itself?

STOP

Understand

1. What is a regular octagon? An 8-sided figure with all sides and all angles congruent.
2. Why will you ignore the word STOP in the center of the sign? Question concerns octagon's shape, not design inside this particular octagon.

Plan

3. How can you tell if the octagon rotates onto itself? Possible answer: All sides and angles coincide.
4. How many times can an octagon rotate on itself? Count the final turn to return to the original position. 8 times.
5. How many degrees are in a complete rotation? 360°
6. How can you find the number of degrees in each turn? Divide 360° by 8.

Solve

7. List the degrees of the rotations.
   45°, 90°, 135°, 180°, 225°, 270°, 315°, 360°

Look Back

8. How can you check your answer? Possible answer: Trace figure on another paper. Turn it on drawing to count rotations.

SOLVE ANOTHER PROBLEM

How many degrees does it take for a regular hexagon to rotate onto itself?

60°, 120°, 180°, 240°, 300°, 360°

Name ______

Guided Problem Solving 11-9

GPS **PROBLEM 11, STUDENT PAGE 614**

A flooring contractor has 175 tiles that are 6 in. by 6 in. for covering a kitchen floor that is 15 ft by 10 ft. Does he have enough tiles? Explain.

Possible answer: Item 10

Understand

1. How many tiles does the contractor have? 175 tiles.
2. What are the dimensions of each tile? 6 in. by 6 in.
3. What are the dimensions of the floor? 15 ft by 10 ft.

Plan

4. Use decimals to write the dimensions of the tiles in feet. 0.5 ft by 0.5 ft.
5. What is the area of each tile in square feet? 0.25 ft^2
6. What is the area of the kitchen floor? 150 ft^2
7. How can you find the number of tiles needed to cover the floor? Divide 150 by 0.25.

Solve

8. How many tiles are needed to cover the floor? 600 tiles.
9. Does he have enough tiles? Explain. No, he needs 600 tiles but only has 175 tiles.

Look Back

10. How could you find the answer in another way? Convert measures to inches and compute: 21,600 ÷ 36 = 600.

SOLVE ANOTHER PROBLEM

A section of a kitchen wall is 4 ft by 7 ft. It will be covered with tiles that are 3 in. by 3 in. The contractor has 450 tiles. Does she have enough tiles? Explain.

Yes, she needs 448 tiles and has 450 tiles on hand.

Name ______

Guided Problem Solving 12-1

GPS **PROBLEM 11, STUDENT PAGE 630**

One word is to be chosen from each list. How many sentences can be made?

article	adjective	noun	verb	adverb
The	quick	dog	ran	quickly
A	smelly	robot	slipped	badly
	purple	king	cooked	
	scraggly		scratched	
			waited	

Understand Possible answer: Items 4 and 7

1. How many words are in each list?
   a. Article 2 words. b. Adjective 4 words. c. Noun 3 words.
   d. Verb 5 words. e. Adverb 2 words.
2. How many words will be chosen from each list? One word.
3. Do you need to be concerned with how well the sentences read? No.

Plan

4. How can you use the Counting Principle to find the number of sentences? Multiply the number of words in each list.
5. Write an expression to find the number of sentences. $2 \times 4 \times 3 \times 5 \times 2$

Solve

6. Simplify your expression in Item 5. How many sentences can be made. 240 sentences.

Look Back

7. What is a different way to find the answer? Which way is easier? Explain. Tree diagram; Counting Principle is easier because there are a lot of choices.

SOLVE ANOTHER PROBLEM

School shirts can be ordered through the Student Council. How many different shirts are possible?

color	sleeve	size	style	design
blue	short	small	tee	name only
gold	long	medium	sweat	name and logo
		large	jersey	
		x-large		

96 shirts.

Name ______

Guided Problem Solving 12-2

GPS **PROBLEM 22, STUDENT PAGE 636**

Mr. Lehr has 8 groups in his math class. Tomorrow, 3 of the groups will give their group-project reports. How many different ways can he select and order the groups?

Understand

1. How many groups are in the class? 8 groups.
2. How many groups will give reports tomorrow? 3 groups.
3. What are you asked to find? How many different ways Mr. Lehr can choose to order groups reporting on their products.

Plan

4. How many groups will *not* give reports tomorrow? 5 groups.
5. Use factorial notation to write the number of ways to order
   a. all the groups. 8!   b. the groups not selected. 5!
6. Use factorial notation to write an expression to show how many different ways Mr. Lehr can select and order the groups. $\frac{8!}{5!}$

Solve

7. How many different ways can Mr. Lehr select and order the groups? 336 ways.
8. Write a sentence to give the final answer. Mr. Lehr can select and order the groups in 336 ways.

Look Back

9. Rewrite the expression in Item 6 using factors instead of factorial notation.
   $\frac{8 \times 7 \times 6 \times 5 \times 4 \times 3 \times 2 \times 1}{5 \times 4 \times 3 \times 2 \times 1}$

SOLVE ANOTHER PROBLEM

Mrs. Lenzi has 7 groups in her math class. Next Monday, 4 of the groups will give their group-project reports. How many different ways can she select and order the groups? 840 ways.

Name ______________________

Guided Problem Solving 12-3

GPS PROBLEM 11, STUDENT PAGE 641

How many ways could you select (3) possible components for a sound system from a tape-deck, CD player, laser disk, equalizer, and surround-sound stereo?

Understand

1. Circle the number of components that will be in the sound system.
2. Underline the possible components to include in the system.
3. Are you asked for how the system can be assembled or the number of ways it can be assembled? Number of ways.

Plan

4. Write each in factorial notation.
   - a. number of ways to select and arrange all components 5!
   - b. number of ways to arrange the selected components 3!
   - c. number of ways to arrange the components that are *not* selected 2!
5. Which shows the number of ways to assemble the sound system? b
   - a. $\frac{5!}{3!}$
   - b. $\frac{5!}{3! \times 2!}$
   - c. $\frac{3! \times 2!}{5!}$
   - d. $\frac{3!}{2!}$

Solve

6. How many ways could you select 3 components for the sound-system? 10 ways.

Look Back

7. Check your answer by making a list of the possible sound-system components. Use *T*, *C*, *L*, *E*, and *S* to represent the components.
   TCL; TCE; TCS; TLE; TLS; TES; CLE; CLS; CES; LES

SOLVE ANOTHER PROBLEM

How many ways could you make a hamburger with 4 toppings if the available toppings are tomato, cheese, onion, pickle, lettuce, bacon, and relish? 35 ways.

Name ______________________

Guided Problem Solving 12-4

GPS PROBLEM 14, STUDENT PAGE 650

The yellow and green sectors of the spinner are each $\frac{1}{4}$ of the spinner area.

What is the probability of not spinning green?

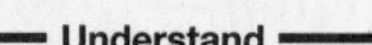

Yellow

Green

Red

Understand

1. How many sections are shown on the spinner? 3 sectors.
2. Which sectors have the same area? Yellow and green sectors.
3. What fraction of the area is red? $\frac{1}{2}$

Plan

4. How can you make the red sector have the same area as the green sector? Divide it in half.
5. How can you find the probability of an event? a
   - a. $P = \frac{\text{number of outcomes in the event}}{\text{number of outcomes in sample space}}$
   - b. $P = \frac{\text{number of events}}{\text{number of events in sample space}}$
6. List the equally-likely outcomes. Some colors may be listed more than one time. Red, red, green, yellow.
7. List the outcomes that are *not* green. Red, red, yellow.

Solve

8. Write the probability of not spinning green as a fraction. $\frac{3}{4}$

Look Back

9. How can you use subtraction to find the answer? Find the probability of spinning green and subtract from 1.

SOLVE ANOTHER PROBLEM

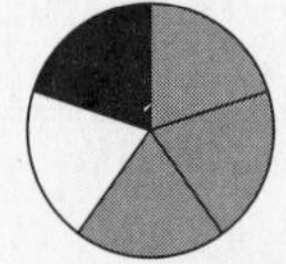

The white and black sectors of the spinner are each $\frac{1}{5}$ of the spinner area. What is the probability of not spinning black? $\frac{4}{5}$

Name ______________________

Guided Problem Solving 12-5

GPS PROBLEM 11, STUDENT PAGE 656

Cliff surveyed his class to find the day of the month each person was born and organized his data in a stem and leaf diagram.

- a. What is the probability that a student was born on the 17th?
- b. What is the probability that a student was born after the 29th?
- c. What is the probability that a student was not born on the 4th?

Stem	Leaf
0	1 3 5 7 7 8 8 9
1	1 1 3 5 6 7 7 7 8 9
2	0 0 1 2 2 3 4 6 6 7 8 9 9
3	0 0 1

Understand

1. What does each response represent? Birthdate of one student.

Plan

2. How many outcomes are in the sample space? 33 outcomes.
3. Write the number of students that were born each date.
   - a. 17th 3 students.
   - b. 30th or 31st 3 students.
   - c. 4th 0 students.
4. How many students were *not* born on the 4th? 33 students.

Solve

5. Write the probability that a student was born on each given date.
   - a. 17th $\frac{3}{33}$ or $\frac{1}{11}$
   - b. after the 29th $\frac{3}{33}$ or $\frac{1}{11}$
   - c. not on 4th 1

Look Back

6. Write each probability in Item 5 as a percent.
   - a. 17th $9.\overline{09}\%$
   - b. after the 29th $9.\overline{09}\%$
   - c. not on 4th 100%

SOLVE ANOTHER PROBLEM

Add two more birthdates, the ninth and the twenty-ninth to Cliff's stem and leaf diagram above. Then answer the questions below.

- a. What is the probability that a student was born on the 25th? 0
- b. What is the probability that a student was born after the 16th? $\frac{21}{35} = \frac{3}{5}$
- c. What is the probability that a student was not born on the 10th? 1

Name ______________________

Guided Problem Solving 12-6

GPS PROBLEM 7, STUDENT PAGE 661

You roll a pair of number cubes in a board game. If the first cube comes up a (6), find the probability that the sum of the two number cubes is:

a. 6 b. 7 c. greater than 10 d. greater than 6

Understand

1. How many number cubes will you roll? 2 number cubes.
2. Circle the number that came up when the first cube was rolled.

Plan

3. What are the possible outcomes for the second number cube? 1, 2, 3, 4, 5, 6
4. List the possible outcomes for the two rolls.
   - a. 6 + 1 = 7
   - b. 6 + 2 = 8
   - c. 6 + 3 = 9
   - d. 6 + 4 = 10
   - e. 6 + 5 = 11
   - f. 6 + 6 = 12
5. Which sums are greater than 10? 11, 12 Greater than 6? 7–12

Solve

6. Use the data in Item 4 to find each probability.
   - a. $P(\text{sum is } 6) = 0$
   - b. $P(\text{sum is } 7) = \frac{1}{6}$
   - c. $P(\text{sum} > 10) = \frac{2}{6} = \frac{1}{3}$
   - d. $P(\text{sum is} > 6) = 1$

Look Back

7. Which probability can you determine without listing the possible outcomes in Item 4? Explain. Possible answer: *P*(sum is 6), since any roll of second cube gives a sum > 6, so probability is 0.

SOLVE ANOTHER PROBLEM

You roll a pair of number cubes in a board game. If the first cube comes up a 4, find the probability that the sum of the two number cubes is:

- a. 6 $\frac{1}{6}$
- b. 11 0
- c. less than 8 $\frac{1}{2}$
- d. greater than 5 $\frac{5}{6}$

Name ____________________

Guided Problem Solving
12-7

GPS PROBLEM 17, STUDENT PAGE 667

You enter a contest on your birthday. Suppose you win a prize in the contest.

a. If the prizes are chosen at random, what is your chance of winning the concert tickets?

b. If the first place winner chose the graphing calculator, what are your chances of winning the concert tickets now?

PRIZES!
Concert Tickets
Graphing Calculator
Computer Game
3 music CDs
Dinner for 2

Understand

1. How many different prizes are possible? 5 prizes.

2. How are the prizes awarded? Randomly.

3. Is the prize awarded to subsequent winners dependent or independent of the prizes awarded to prior winners? Dependent.

Plan

4. How many outcomes (prizes) are available to the first winner? 5 prizes.

5. How many outcomes are available to the second winner? 4 prizes.

6. How many outcomes (prizes) can you win? 1 prize.

Solve

7. What is your chance of getting the concert tickets if you are the first winner? 1 in 5.

8. If you are the second winner, what are your chances of winning concert tickets if the calculator has already been awarded? 1 in 4.

Look Back

9. As other prizes are awarded to other winners, are you more or less likely to win the concert tickets? Explain.

More likely, since sample space is smaller.

SOLVE ANOTHER PROBLEM

Prizes at a raffle are \$100, \$75, \$25, \$25, \$25, and \$25.

a. If the prizes are chosen at random, what is your chance of winning \$75? 1 in 6.

b. If the \$100 prize has already been won, what are your chances of winning \$75? 1 in 5.

DATE DUE
